# STUDY AND REVISE

## AS/A2 Level

# Chemistry

First published 2000
exclusively for WHSmith by

Hodder and Stoughton Educational
338 Euston Road
LONDON NW1 3BH

A CIP record for this book is available from the British Library

Text: Andrew Hunt with Tony Buzan
Mind Maps: The Buzan Centres

ISBN 0-340-746912

10 9 8 7 6 5
Year    2005    2004

Typeset by Wearset, Boldon, Tyne and Wear

Printed and bound in Great Britain for Hodder & Stoughton Educational by
The Bath Press, Bath.

# CONTENTS

**Revision for A Level success**                                v
by Tony Buzan

**A-level Chemistry and this revision guide**                  ix

**Chapter 1**   **Atomic structure**                           **1**
                Atoms and isotopes                              1
                Mass spectrometer                               2
                Electrons in atoms                              3

**Chapter 2**   **Chemical quantities**                        **6**
                Chemical amounts in moles                       6
                The Avogadro constant                          6
                Molar masses                                    8
                Finding formulae                                8
                Equations                                       9
                Calculations from equations                    10
                Volumes of gases                                12
                Concentrations                                  13
                Acid-base titrations                            14

**Chapter 3**   **Structure and bonding**                      **16**
                States of matter                                16
                Giant or molecular?                             18
                Structure and bonding in metals                18
                Structure and bonding in compounds
                of metals with non-metals                       19
                Covalent bonding                                21
                Intermolecular forces                           24
                Structures based on covalent
                bonding                                         26
                In-between types of bonding                     28

**Chapter 4**   **Energetics**                                 **30**
                Enthalpy changes                                30
                Calorimetry                                     31
                Standard enthalpy changes                       33
                Hess's law cycles                               34
                Enthalpy changes and covalent
                bonding                                         36
                Stability                                       37

**Chapter 5**   **Redox reactions**                            **39**
                Electron transfer                               39
                Oxidation numbers                               40

**Chapter 6**   **Periodicity**                                **43**
                The periodic table                              43
                Periodicity of physical properties
                of the elements                                 43
                Periodicity in the properties of atoms  45

**Chapter 7**   **The s-block elements**                       **48**
                Acids and alkalis                               48
                Group 1                                         49

                Group 2                                         50
                Thermal stability                               52

**Chapter 8**   **The halogens**                               **53**
                Halogen elements                                53
                Halogen compounds                               54
                Oxoanions of chlorine                           55
                Bleach                                          56
                Manufacture of halogens                         57

**Chapter 9**   **Extraction of metals**                       **59**
                Extraction of iron from its oxide
                using carbon                                    59
                Extraction of aluminium by
                electrolysis                                    60
                Extraction of titanium by reduction
                of its chloride                                 61
                Recycling                                       61

**Chapter 10**  **Reaction rates**                             **63**
                Factors affecting rates of reaction            63
                Collision theory                                64
                Kinetic stability                               66

**Chapter 11**  **Chemical equilibrium**                       **68**
                Reversible reactions                            68
                Dynamic equilibrium                             68
                Factors affecting the position of
                equilibrium                                     69
                Chemical equilibrium in industry               70

**Chapter 12**  **Organic molecules**                          **73**
                Organic molecules                               73
                Organic names                                   74
                Isomerism                                       75

**Chapter 13**  **Hydrocarbons**                               **77**
                Alkanes                                         77
                Free-radical substitution reactions            78
                Alkenes                                         78
                Electrophilic addition reactions               80
                Addition polymerisation                         81

**Chapter 14**  **Halogenoalkanes**                            **82**
                Structures and names of
                halogenoalkanes                                 82
                Properties of halogenoalkanes                   82
                Reaction mechanisms                             84
                Uses of halogenoalkanes                         84

**Chapter 15**  **Alcohols**                                   **85**
                Structures and names of alcohols               85
                Properties of alcohols                          85
                Manufacture and uses of alcohols               87

# CONTENTS

**Chapter 16** | **Fuels and chemicals from oil** | **88**
Oil and refining | 88
Fuels from oil | 88
Chemicals from oil | 89

**Chapter 17** | **Waste from organic chemicals** | **91**
Wastes from burning fuels | 91
Recycling or dumping solid waste | 92

**Chapter 18** | **Reaction kinetics** | **94**
Investigating reaction rates | 94
Rate equations | 94
Determining reaction orders | 96
The effect of temperature on rates | 98
Rates and reaction mechanisms | 99

**Chapter 19** | **The equilibrium law** | **100**
Equilibrium constants, $K_c$ | 100
Equilibrium constants, $K_p$ | 101
Heterogeneous equilibria | 103
Effects of changing conditions
on equilibria | 103

**Chapter 20** | **Acid-base equilibria** | **105**
The Brønsted-Lowry theory | 105
pH 106
Weak acids and bases | 108
Acid-base titrations | 109
Buffer solutions | 111

**Chapter 21** | **Redox equilibria** | **113**
Electrochemical cells | 113
Electrode potentials | 114
An electrochemical series | 115
Cells and batteries | 117
Corrosion | 118

**Chapter 22** | **Thermochemistry of ionic
compounds** | **120**
The Born-Haber cycle | 120
Energy changes during dissolving | 122

**Chapter 23** | **Energetics and the direction of
change** | **124**
Spontaneous changes | 124
Entropy | 124
Free energy | 125
Alternative tests of feasibility | 125
Thermodynamic stability | 126

**Chapter 24** | **Periodic patterns and trends** | **127**
Periodicity of the chemical
properties of elements | 127
Periodicity in the properties of
oxides | 127
Periodicity in the properties of
chlorides | 128
Group 4 | 128

**Chapter 25** | **Transition metal chemistry** | **130**
Elements of the d-block | 130
Variable oxidation states | 131
Complex ions | 132
Coloured ions | 135
Catalysis | 136

**Chapter 26** | **Stereoisomerism** | **138**
Structural isomerism | 138
Geometrical isomerism | 138
Optical isomerism | 138

**Chapter 27** | **Arenes** | **141**
Aromatic hydrocarbons | 141
Electrophilic substitution | 143
Phenol | 144

**Chapter 28** | **Carbonyl compounds** | **146**
Aldehydes and ketones | 146
Nucleophilic addition reactions | 147
Identifying carbonyl compounds | 148

**Chapter 29** | **Carboxylic acids and related
compounds** | **150**
Carboxylic acids | 150
Acylation | 151
Addition-elimination reactions | 152
Esters | 152

**Chapter 30** | **Organic nitrogen compounds** | **154**
Alkyl (aliphatic) amines | 154
Aryl (aromatic) amines | 155
Base strength of amines | 156
Amino acids and proteins | 156

**Chapter 31** | **Polymers** | **158**
Polymers | 158
Addition polymers | 158
Condensation polymers | 159
Polymer properties and uses | 161

**Chapter 32** | **Organic synthesis** | **162**
Organic routes | 162
Practical techniques | 163
Tests for functional groups | 164

**Chapter 33** | **Instrumental analysis** | **166**
Mass spectrometer | 166
Infra-red spectra | 166
Ultraviolet and visible spectra | 167
Nuclear magnetic resonance
spectra | 168

**Answers to questions** | **170**

**Matching your revision to your course
specification** | **184**

**Index** | **187**

**Periodic table** | **190**

You are now in the most important educational stage of your life and are soon to take exams that may have a major impact on your future career and goals. As one A Level student put it: 'It's crunch time!'

At this crucial stage of your life, the thing you need even more than subject knowledge is the knowledge of **how** to remember, **how** to read faster, **how** to comprehend, **how** to study, **how** to take notes and **how** to organise your thoughts. You need to know how to **think**; you need a basic introduction on how to use that super computer inside your head – your brain.

The next few pages contain a goldmine of information on how you can achieve success, both at school and in your A Level exams, as well as in your professional or university career. These pages will give you information on memory, thinking skills, speed reading and study that will enable you to be successful in all your academic pursuits. You will learn:

1   How to remember more *while* you are learning.

2   How to remember more *after* you have finished a class or a study period.

3   How to use special techniques to improve your memory.

4   How to use a revolutionary note-taking technique called Mind Maps that will double your memory and help you to write essays and answer exam questions.

5   How to read everything faster, while at the same time improving comprehension and concentration.

6   How to zap your revision.

## How to understand, improve and master your memory

Your memory really is like a muscle. Don't exercise it and it will grow weaker; do exercise it and it will grow incredibly more powerful. There are really only four main things you need to understand about your memory in order to increase its power dramatically:

### 1 Recall during learning – you must take breaks!

When you are studying, your memory can concentrate, understand and remember well for between 20 and 45 minutes at a time. Then it needs a break. If you carry on for longer than this without one, your memory starts to break down. If you study for hours non-stop, you will remember only a fraction of what you have been trying to learn and you will have wasted valuable revision time.

So, ideally, *study for less than an hour*, then take a five- to ten-minute break. During this break, listen to music, go for a walk, do some exercise or just daydream. (Daydreaming is a necessary brainpower booster – geniuses do it regularly.)

During the break your brain will be sorting out what it has been learning and you will go back to your study with the new information safely stored and organised in your memory banks.

Make sure you take breaks at regular intervals as you work through your *Study and Revise AS and A2 Level* book.

### 2 Recall after learning – surfing the waves of your memory

What do you think begins to happen to your memory straight after you have finished learning something? Does it immediately start forgetting? No! Your brain actually *increases* its power and carries on remembering. For a short time after your study session, your brain integrates the information making a more complete picture of everything it has just learnt. Only then does the rapid decline in memory begin, and as much as 80% of what you have learnt can be forgotten in a day.

However, if you catch the top of the wave of your memory, and briefly review back what you have been revising at the correct time, the memory is stamped in far more strongly and stays at the crest of the wave for much longer. To maximise your brain's power to remember, take a few minutes and use a Mind Map to review what you have learnt at the end of a day. Then review it at the end of a week, again at the end of a month and, finally, a week before the exams. That way you'll surf-ride your memory wave all the way to your exam, success, and beyond!

### 3 The memory principle of association

The muscle of your memory becomes stronger when it can **associate** – when it can link things together.

Think about your best friend and all the things your mind automatically links with that person. Think about your favourite hobby and all the associations your mind has when you think about (remember) that hobby.

When you are studying, use this memory principle to make associations between the elements in your subjects and to thus improve both your memory and your chances of success.

### 4 The memory principle of imagination

The muscle of your memory will improve significantly if you can produce big **images** in your mind. Rather than just memorising the name of an historical character, **imagine** that character as if you were a video producer filming that person's life.

In *all* your subjects, use the **imagination** memory principle.

## Your new success formula: Mind Maps®

You have noticed that when people go on holidays or travels they take maps. Why? To give them a general picture of where they are going, to help them locate places of special interest and importance, to help them find things more easily and to help them remember distances, locations and so on.

It is exactly the same with your mind and with study.

If you have a 'map of the territory' of what you have to learn, then everything is easier. In learning and study, the Mind Map is that special tool.

As well as helping you with all areas of study, the Mind Map actually *mirrors the way your brain works*. Your Mind Maps can be used for taking notes from your study books, taking notes in class, preparing your homework, presenting your homework, reviewing your tests, checking your and your friends' knowledge in any subject, and for *helping you understand anything you learn.*

As you will see, Mind Maps use, throughout, Imagination and Association. As such, they automatically strengthen your memory muscle every time you use them. Throughout this *Study and Revise AS and A2 Level* book you will find Mind Maps that summarise the most important areas of the subject you are studying. Study them, add some colour, personalise them, and then have a go at drawing your own – you will remember them far better! Put them on your walls and in your files for a quick and easy review of the topic.

### Using Mind Maps

Mind Maps are a versatile tool – use them for taking notes in class or from books, for solving problems, for brainstorming with friends, and for reviewing and revising for exams – their uses are infinite! You will find them invaluable for planning essays for coursework and exams. Number your main branches in the order in which you want to use them and off you go – the main headings for your essay are done *and* all your ideas are logically organised.

## Super speed reading and study

What happens to your comprehension as your reading speed rises? 'It goes down.' Wrong! It seems incredible, but it has been proved that the faster you read, the more you comprehend and remember.

So here are some tips to help you to practise reading faster – you'll cover the ground much more quickly, remember more *and* have more time for revision and leisure activities.

### How to make study easy for your brain

When you are going somewhere, is it easier to know beforehand where you are going, or not? Obviously it is easier if you do know. It is the same for your brain and a book. When you get a new book, there are seven things you can do to help your brain get to 'know the territory' faster.

1   Scan through the whole book in less than 20 minutes, as you would do if you were in a shop thinking whether or not to buy it. This gives your brain control.

2   Think about what you already know about the subject. You'll often find out it's a lot more than you thought. A good way of doing this is to draw a quick Mind Map on everything you know after you have skimmed through it.

### How to draw a Mind Map

1   Start in the middle of the page with the paper turned sideways. This gives your brain more radiant freedom for its thoughts.

2   Always start by drawing a picture or symbol. Why? Because **a picture is worth a thousand words to your brain**. Try to use at least three colours, as colour helps your memory even more.

3   Let your thoughts flow, and write or draw your ideas on coloured branching lines connected to your central image. These key symbols and words are the headings for your topic.

4   Next, add facts and ideas by drawing more, smaller, branches on to the appropriate main branches, just like a tree.

5   Always print each word clearly on its line. Use only one word per line.

6   To link ideas and thoughts on different branches, use arrows, colours, underlining and boxes.

### How to read a Mind Map

1   Begin in the centre, the focus of your topic.

2   The words/images attached to the centre are like chapter headings; read them next.

3   Always read out from the centre, in every direction (even on the left-hand side, where you will have to read from right to left; instead of the usual left to right).

3 Ask who, what, why, where, when and how questions about what is in the book. Questions help your brain 'fish' the knowledge out.

4 Ask your friends what they know about the subject. This helps them review the knowledge in their own brains and helps your brain get new knowledge about what you are studying.

5 Have another quick speed through the book, this time looking for any diagrams, pictures and illustrations, and also at the beginnings and ends of chapters. Most information is contained in the beginnings and ends.

6 Build up a Mind Map as you study the book. This helps your brain organise and hold (remember) information as you study.

7 If you come across any difficult parts in your book, mark them and move on. Your brain *will* be able to solve the problems when you come back to them a little bit later, much like saving the difficult bits of a jigsaw puzzle for later. When you have finished the book, quickly review it one more time and then discuss it with friends. This will lodge it permanently in your memory banks.

### Super speed reading

1 First read the whole text (whether it's a lengthy book or an exam paper) very quickly, to give your brain an overall idea of what's ahead and get it working. (It's like sending out a scout to look at the territory you have to cover – it's much easier when you know what to expect.) Then read the text again for more detailed information.

2 Have the text a reasonable distance away from your eyes. In this way your eye/brain system will be able to see more at a glance and will naturally begin to read faster.

3 Take in groups of words at a time. Rather than reading 'slowly and carefully', read faster, more enthusiastically. Your comprehension will rocket!

4 Take in phrases rather than single words while you read.

5 Use a guide. Your eyes are designed to follow movement, so a thin pencil underneath the lines you are reading, moved smoothly along, will 'pull' your eyes to faster speeds.

## Helpful hints for exam revision

To avoid exam panic, cram at the start of your course, not the end. It takes the same amount of time, so you may as well use it where it is best placed!

Use Mind Maps throughout your course and build a Master Mind Map for each subject – a giant Mind Map that summarises everything you know about the subject.

Use memory techniques, such as mnemonics (verses or systems for remembering things like dates and events or lists).

Get together with one or two friends to revise, compare Mind Maps and discuss topics.

### And finally . . .

- *Have fun while you learn* – studies show that those people who enjoy what they are doing understand and remember it more and generally do better.

- *Use your teachers* as resource centres. Ask them for help with specific topics and with more general advice on how you can improve your all-round performance.

- *Personalise your Study and Revise AS and A2 Level book* by underlining and highlighting, by adding notes and pictures. Allow your brain to have a conversation with it!

### Your amazing brain and its amazing cells

Your brain is like a super computer. The world's best computers have only a few thousand or hundred thousand computer chips. Your brain has 'computer chips' too; they are called brain cells. Unlike the computer, you do not have only a few thousand computer chips – the number of brain cells in your head is a *million million*! This means you are a genius just waiting to discover yourself! All you have to do is learn how to get those brain cells working together, and you'll not only become more smart, you'll have more free time to pursue your other fun activities.

The more you understand your amazing brain, the more it will repay and amaze you!

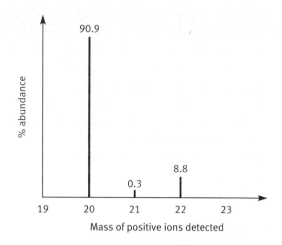

01.04   **Mass spectrum of neon showing the relative abundance of the three isotopes**

## Mass spectrometer

Mass spectrometry helps to investigate the isotopes of an element. Inside a mass spectrometer there is a vacuum so that it is possible to produce and study ionised atoms which do not otherwise exist.

The mass spectrum for an element shows the relative abundance of the isotopes of the element. This makes it possible to calculate the relative atomic mass for the element.

### Average relative atomic masses

Relative atomic masses are not usually whole numbers because elements are mixtures of isotopes.

### Definition

The **relative atomic mass**, $A_r$, of an element is the average mass of the atoms of the element relative to the mass of the atoms of carbon-12 for which $A_r = 12$ exactly.

 *Relative atomic masses do not have units because they are ratios.*

Chlorine has two isotopes: chlorine-35 and chlorine-37. Naturally occurring chlorine contains 75% of chlorine-35 and 25% of chlorine 37.

The average relative atomic mass of chlorine

$$= \frac{(75 \times 35) + (25 \times 37)}{100} = 35.5$$

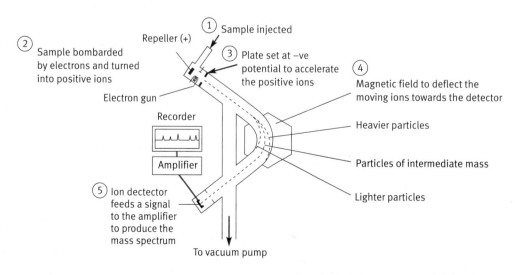

01.03   **Diagram of a mass spectrometer showing the main stages in producing a mass spectrum**

## Electrons in atoms

The electrons in atoms occupy atomic orbitals. Each orbital has:

- a definite energy
- a characteristic shape.

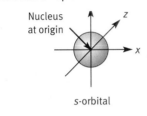

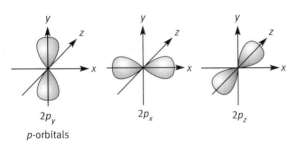

**01.05   Shapes of s and p orbitals. Every shell has one s orbital. The second and higher shells have three p orbitals**

The orbitals are grouped into sub-shells and main shells. A sub-shell consists of orbitals of the same type: s, p, d or f.

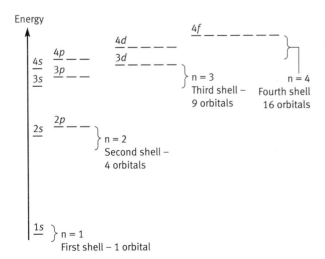

**01.06   The relative energies of the atomic orbitals in atoms**

ℹ️ *Chemists also use the terms **levels** and **sub-levels** to describe shells and sub-shells.*

### Factfile

**Rules**

Three rules govern the way that electrons fill the orbitals.

- An electron goes into the lowest available energy level.
- Each orbital can only hold two electrons, with opposite spins.
- Where there two or more orbitals with the same energy they fill singly, with parallel spins, before the electrons pair up.

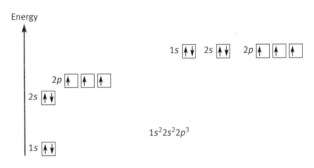

**01.07   Three ways of representing the electron configuration of nitrogen. Note that the total number of electrons equals the atomic number of the element. Note too that the three p orbitals are filled singly**

### Definition

The **electron configuration** of an element describes the number and arrangement of electrons in its atoms.

The spin of an electron makes it behave like a tiny magnet that can line up in a magnetic field, either with the field (spin up, ↑) or against the field (spin down, ↓).

The electrons in the outer shell of an atom help to determine its chemical properties. Elements in the same group of the periodic table have similar properties because they have the same outer electron configuration.

ℹ️ *All atoms of the metals in Group 2 have the outer electron configuration: $s^2$.*

## Ionisation energies

It is possible to measure the minimum energy needed to remove an electron from free, gaseous atoms. This is the first ionisation energy of the atoms.

**Definition**

The first **ionisation energy** for an element is the energy needed to remove one mole of electrons from one mole of gaseous atoms. Successive ionisation energies for the same element measure the energy per mole needed to remove a second, third, fourth electron and so on.

$Na(g) \rightarrow Na^+(g) + e^-$
1st ionisation energy $= +496$ kJ mol$^{-1}$

$Na^+(g) \rightarrow Na^{2+}(g) + e^-$
2nd ionisation energy $= +4563$ kJ mol$^{-1}$

$Na^{2+}(g) \rightarrow Na^{3+}(g) + e^-$
3rd ionisation energy $= +6913$ kJ mol$^{-1}$

The successive ionisation energies for an element get bigger and bigger. This is not surprising because having removed one electron it is more difficult to remove a second electron from the positive ion formed.

There are eleven electrons in a sodium atom so there are eleven successive ionisation energies for this element.

The graph in Figure 01.08 supports the theory that the electrons in an atom are arranged in a series of energy levels or shells around the nucleus. There are big jumps in value each time electrons start to be removed from the next energy level, or shell, in towards the nucleus.

So, for a sodium atom, there is one electron in the outer shell which is furthest from the nucleus. This outer electron is shielded from the full attraction of

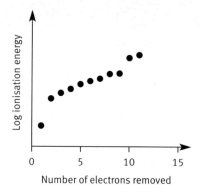

01.08 A plot of log (ionisation energy) against number of electrons removed for sodium. A log plot makes the vertical scale more manageable

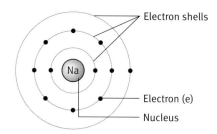

01.09 The electrons in shells for a sodium atom. This diagram only shows the main shells and not the sub-shells

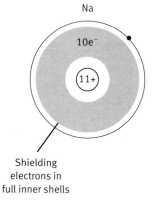

01.10 The shielding effect of electrons in inner shells reducing the pull of the nucleus on the electron in the outer shell

the positive nucleus by ten inner electrons. There are eight electrons in the second shell which are closer to the nucleus and only have two inner shielding electrons. The two inner electrons feel the full attraction of the nuclear charge and are closest to the nucleus. They are the hardest to remove.

## Definition

Shielding is the effect of electrons in inner shells that reduces the pull of the nucleus on the electrons in the outer shell of an atom. Thanks to shielding, the electrons in the outer shell are attracted by an 'effective nuclear charge', which is less than the full charge on the nucleus.

## REVIEW

**Make your own Mind Map to summarise the key ideas about atomic structure. You can use Figure 01.11 as your starting point**

**Answer the 'test yourself' questions to revise the ideas in this topic. Check your answers against the solutions on page 170. Where you feel the need for more practice, look for more examples in past examination papers and text books.**

## TEST YOURSELF

8  **The five ionisation energies of an element in kJ mol⁻¹ are: 801, 2427, 3660, 25 026 and 32 828. How many electrons are there in the outer shell of the atoms of this element? To which group of the periodic table does this element belong?**

9  **Sketch a graph of log (ionisation energy/kJ mol⁻¹) against number of electrons removed when all the electrons are successively removed from a magnesium atom.**

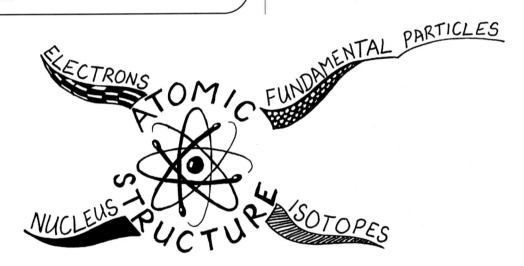

**01.11   Starting point for an atomic structure Mind Map**

## PREVIEW

By the end of this topic you will be able to:

✔ understand how chemists measure amounts of substances in moles

✔ define the Avogadro constant

✔ understand the term molar mass

✔ use data to determine the empirical and molecular formulae of compounds

✔ write balanced equations

✔ use equations to work out reacting masses of chemicals

✔ work out reacting gas volumes from equations

✔ understand what is meant by the molar volume of a gas and be able to use molar volumes of gases in calculations

✔ use information about the concentrations of solutions in mol dm$^{-3}$ and g dm$^{-3}$

✔ interpret the results of acid-base titrations.

## Chemical amounts in moles

Chemists use measurements to find formulae and write equations. They can only do this by working with amounts of chemicals that contain equal numbers of atoms, molecules or ions. So chemists measure amounts in moles.

ℹ *The mole is the chemist's term for a 'heap' of stuff containing a particular number of atoms, molecules, ions or any other type of particle.*

The mole is the unit for amount of substance.

## Definition

**One mole** is the amount of substance that contains as many atoms, molecules or ions as there are atoms in exactly 12 g of the carbon-12 isotope.

Unfortunately there are no measuring instruments for determining chemical amounts directly, unlike balances for determining masses in kilograms or graduated glassware for measuring volumes in dm$^3$ (litres). Instead, chemists first measure masses or volumes and then calculate the amount that contains the agreed number of atoms, molecules or ions.

## Mind Map

The Mind Map on page 7 will help you to keep track of all the chemical calculations you are expected to be able to do. Make your own colourful copy of the Mind Map, a bit at a time. Work outwards from the middle, adding the sections one by one as you work through this topic. Add notes around the Mind Map, such as definitions and key relationships. Add more sketches to make the map more memorable.

## The Avogadro constant

The number of atoms in one mole of an element is the Avogadro constant.

## Definition

The value of the **Avogadro constant**, *L*, $= 6.02 \times 10^{23}$ mol$^{-1}$.

This is also the number of molecules in a mole of a molecular compound such as water or the number of ions in a mole of ions.

ℹ *The Avogadro constant is the number of particles per mole – so it does have units (mol$^{-1}$).*

Always make sure that you state which particles are involved. In 18 g water (1 mol of $H_2O$) there are $6.02 \times 10^{23}$ water molecules made from $12.04 \times 10^{23}$ hydrogen atoms bonded to $= 6.02 \times 10^{23}$ oxygen atoms.

## WORKED EXAMPLE

How many iron atoms are there in 0.75 mol of iron?

### Note on the method

Use this relationship:

number of atoms, molecules or ions = amount of substance/ mol × Avogadro constant/ mol$^{-1}$

### Answer

0.75 mol iron atoms, Fe, contains
0.75 mol × (6.02 × 10$^{23}$ mol$^{-1}$) atoms
= 4.5 × 10$^{23}$ atoms.

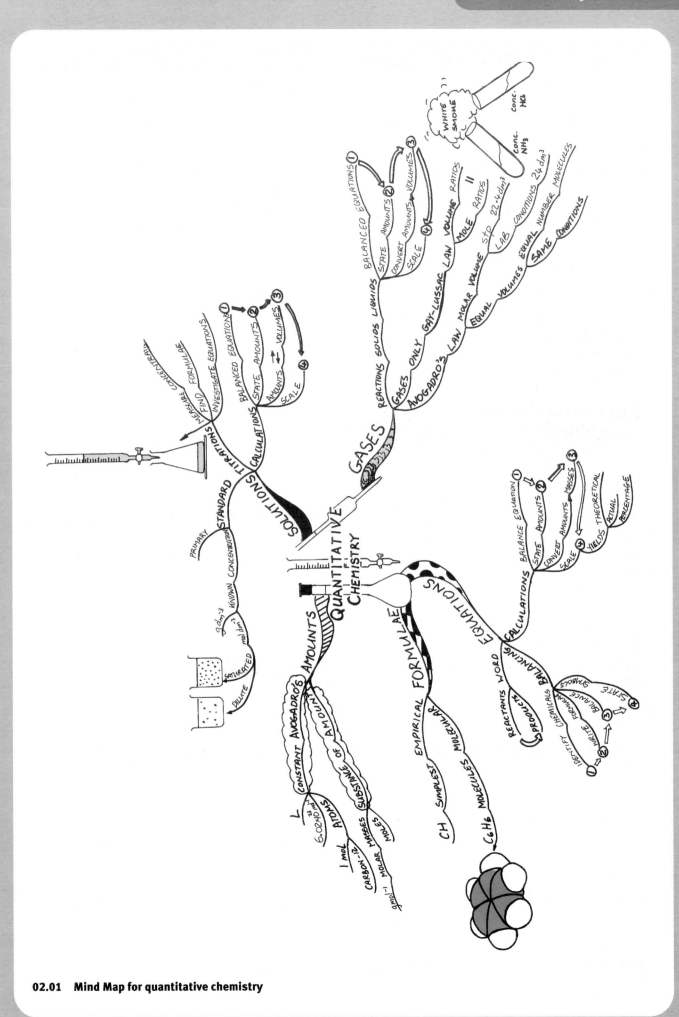

**02.01    Mind Map for quantitative chemistry**

1 How many:
   a carbon atoms are there in 0.25 mol carbon atoms?
   b oxygen atoms are there in 2 mol oxygen gas, $O_2$?
   c water molecules are there 3 mol water, $H_2O$?
   d chloride ions are there in 1 mol magnesium chloride, $MgCl_2$?

2 How many moles of:
   a atoms are there in 14 g iron?
   b molecules are there in 11 g carbon dioxide, $CO_2$?
   c sodium ions are there in 10 g sodium hydroxide, NaOH?

3 What is the mass of:
   a 3 mol of iron(II) chloride, $FeCl_2$?
   b 0.5 mol of nitric acid, $HNO_3$?
   c 0.01 mol of ethene, $C_2H_4$?

## Molar masses

The molar mass for the atoms of an element is equal numerically to the relative atomic mass of the element (see page 2 for a definition and page 184 for a table of values). The relative atomic mass of carbon is 12 so the molar mass of carbon atoms = 12 g mol$^{-1}$.

**Definition**

The **molar mass** is the mass of one mole of a chemical. The symbol for the molar mass is $M$. The unit is g mol$^{-1}$.

**i** *As always with molar quantities you must state exactly the atom, molecule or ion. The molar mass of hydrogen atoms, $M(H) = 1$ g mol$^{-1}$. The molar mass of hydrogen molecules $M(H_2) = 2$ g mol$^{-1}$.*

You calculate the molar mass of any substance by adding up the molar masses of the atoms in the formula.

$$M(H_2O) = [(2 \times 1 \text{ g mol}^{-1}) + 16 \text{ g mol}^{-1}]$$
$$= 18 \text{ g mol}^{-1}$$

$$M(MgSO_4) = [24 \text{ g mol}^{-1} + 32 \text{ g mol}^{-1} + (4 \times 16 \text{ g mol}^{-1})]$$
$$= 120 \text{ g mol}^{-1}$$

$$M(Ca(NO_3)_2) = [40 \text{ g mol}^{-1} + 2 \times (14 + 3 \times 16 \text{ g mol}^{-1})]$$
$$= 164 \text{ g mol}^{-1}$$

Experimentally, molar masses can be measured by mass spectrometry (see Section 33.1).

For any pure substance:

$$\text{amount of substance/mol} = \frac{\text{mass of substance/g}}{\text{molar mass/g mol}^{-1}}$$

This rearranges to:

$$\text{mass of substance/g} = \text{amount of substance/mol} \times \text{molar mass/g mol}^{-1}$$

## Finding formulae

### Empirical formulae

You can look up the formula of any compound you are likely to meet. You are, however, expected to understand how to work out a formula by experiment and calculation.

An experiment to find a formula involves measuring the mass of elements that combine in the compound. From the results you can calculate the experimental, or empirical, formula.

**Definition**

The **empirical formula** shows the simplest ratio of the amounts (in moles) of elements in the compound; it therefore gives the ratio of the numbers of atoms.

Chemists often record their results by showing the percentage by mass of each element in a compound. Analysis of copper pyrites, for example, shows that it consists of 34.6% copper, 30.5% iron and 34.9% sulfur. This means that in 100 g of the mineral there are 34.6 g copper, 30.5 g iron and 34.9 g sulfur.

4 Work out the empirical formula of:
   a the mineral copper pyrites (see text above)
   b silicon oxide, given that 6.0 g of the oxide contains 2.8 g silicon
   c a compound in which 1.38 g sodium combines with 0.96 g sulfur and 1.92 g oxygen
   d an organic compound containing 52.2% carbon, 13.0% hydrogen and 34.8% oxygen.

## WORKED EXAMPLE

Analysis of a sample of sodium oxide if 0.69 g sodium combines with 0.24 g oxygen. What is the formula of the salt?

### Notes on the method

Look up the molar masses of the elements in a book of data (see also the table on page 184).

Recall that:

$$\text{amount of substance/mol} = \frac{\text{mass of substance/g}}{\text{molar mass/g mol}^{-1}}$$

### Answer

|  | sodium | oxygen |
|---|---|---|
| Combining masses | 0.69 g | 0.24 g |
| Molar masses of elements | 23 g mol$^{-1}$ | 16 g mol$^{-1}$ |
| Amounts combined | $\dfrac{0.69 \text{ g}}{23 \text{ g mol}^{-1}}$ | $\dfrac{0.24 \text{ g}}{16 \text{ g mol}^{-1}}$ |
|  | = 0.030 mol | = 0.015 mol |
| Simplest ratio of amounts | 2 | 1 |

The formula is Na$_2$O.

The methods used to analyse organic compounds determine the masses of all the elements in a sample except for oxygen. When calculating the empirical formula of an organic compound chemists assume that any mass not accounted for in the results is made up of oxygen.

## Molecular formulae

For molecular compounds, the relative molecular mass shows whether or not the empirical formula is the same as the molecular formula.

### Definition

The **molecular formula** shows the number of atoms of each element in a molecule.

The molecular formula of chlorine is Cl$_2$, of ammonia is NH$_3$ and of ethanol is C$_2$H$_5$OH.

 *The term **molecular formula** only applies to substances that consist of molecules.*

A molecular formula is always a simple multiple of the empirical formula. Analysis shows that the empirical formula of hexane is C$_3$H$_7$. Experiments show that the relative molecular mass of hexane is 86.

The relative mass of the empirical formula, $M_r(C_3H_7) = (3 \times 12) + (7 \times 1) = 43$. So, the molecular formula is twice the empirical formula. The molecular formula of hexane is C$_6$H$_{14}$.

### TEST YOURSELF

**5** Copy this table and fill in the blanks.

| Substance | Empirical formula | Relative molecular mass | Molecular formula |
|---|---|---|---|
| water |  |  | H$_2$O |
| ethane | CH$_3$ | 30 |  |
| benzene |  |  | C$_6$H$_6$ |
| hydrazine | NH$_2$ | 32 |  |

## Equations

### Word equations

A word equation describes a chemical change in words instead of symbols. Writing word equations identifies the reactants (on the left) and products (on the right), so it is a useful first step towards a balanced equation with symbols.

For example:

sodium + water → sodium hydroxide + hydrogen

*Word equations are a useful way of summarising general patterns of behaviour. For example:*

*acid + metal oxide → salt + water*
*carboxylic acid + alcohol → ester + water.*

## Balanced equations

Balanced equations show the amounts (in moles) of reactants and products involved in chemical reactions. There is no change in the total number of atoms of each element as reactants turn into products during a chemical reaction.

You can follow four steps to write the balanced equations for reactions – for example the reaction of sodium with water.

*Step 1 – Identify the reactants and products by name*

Sodium reacts with water to form sodium hydroxide and hydrogen.

*Step 2 – Write down the correct formulae for reactants and products*

$Na + H_2O \rightarrow NaOH + H_2$

*Step 3 – Balance the numbers of atoms of each element by inspection and by writing numbers in front of the formulae as necessary.*

In this example there must be an even number of hydrogen atoms on the left (in $H_2O$ molecules) so the number on the right must be even too.

$2Na + 2H_2O \rightarrow 2NaOH + H_2$

*Never change any of the formulae to balance an equation.*

Do not add an extra formula to balance an equation without carefully checking that it is right to do so. In some redox equations you may have to add hydrogen ions or water molecules to balance the equation.

*Step 4 – Add state symbols*

$2Na(s) + 2H_2O(l) \rightarrow 2NaOH(aq) + H_2(g)$

The balanced equation shows the amounts (in moles) of reactants and products. In the example, 2 mol sodium atoms react with 2 mol water molecules to give 2 mol sodium hydroxide and 1 mol hydrogen. This is the stoichiometry of the reaction.

*The word **stoichiometry** sounds mysterious but is simply based on Greek words meaning 'element-measure'. Stoichiometry is the basis of quantitative analysis where amounts are measured in moles.*

### TEST YOURSELF

6 Write balanced symbol equations for these reactions:
   a calcium metal with water to form a precipitate of calcium hydroxide and hydrogen
   b calcium hydroxide powder with hydrochloric acid to form calcium chloride solution and water
   c iron(III) oxide with aluminium to form iron metal and aluminium oxide
   d ammonia with oxygen to form nitrogen monoxide gas and steam.

## Calculations from equations

### Reacting masses

You can use the fact that a balanced equation shows the amounts (in moles) of reactants and products to work out the quantities involved in any reaction.

### Factfile

**Solving problems based on equations**

1 Write a balanced equation.

2 In words, state what the equation tells you about the substances in which you are interested.

3 Use molar masses to change amounts in moles to masses in grams.

4 Scale the masses to match the quantities in the question.

### WORKED EXAMPLE

What mass of silver bromide can be made by adding excess sodium bromide solution to a solution containing 3.4 g silver nitrate?

**Answer**

$AgNO_3(aq) + NaBr(aq) \rightarrow AgBr(s) + NaNO_3(aq)$

So 1 mol $AgNO_3(aq)$ reacts to form 1 mol $AgBr(s)$.

$M(AgNO_3) = 108 \text{ g mol}^{-1} + 14 \text{ g mol}^{-1} + (3 \times 16 \text{ g mol}^{-1}) = 170 \text{ g mol}^{-1}$

$M(AgBr) = 108 \text{ g mol}^{-1} + 80 \text{ g mol}^{-1} = 188 \text{ g mol}^{-1}$

So 170 g silver nitrate forms 188 g silver bromide

Hence mass of AgBr formed $= \dfrac{3.4 \text{ g} \times 188 \text{ g}}{170 \text{ g}}$

$= 3.76 \text{ g}$

## TEST YOURSELF

7  a  **What mass of copper forms when 4.0 g copper(II) oxide is reduced to the metal by natural gas?**

   b  **What is the mass of the residue on heating 10.0 g of crystalline barium chloride, $BaCl_2.2H_2O$, until all the water of crystallisation has been driven off?**

   c  **What mass of ethanol, $C_2H_5OH$, can be manufactured when 280 g ethene, $C_2H_4$, combines with steam?**

## Yield calculations

Chemists use yield calculations to assess the efficiency of their chemical syntheses. A perfectly efficient reaction would convert all of the starting material to the desired product. This would give a 100% yield.

Few reactions are completely efficient and most reactions, especially organic reactions, give lower yields. There are several reasons why the overall yield may be low.

• The reaction may be incomplete so that a proportion of the starting chemicals fails to react.

• There may be side reactions producing by-products instead of the required chemical.

• Recovery of all the product from the reaction mixture is usually impossible.

• Some of the product is usually lost during transfer of the chemicals from one container to another.

### Definition

The **theoretical yield** is the mass of product assuming that the reaction goes according to the chemical equation and the synthesis is 100% efficient.

The actual yield is the mass of product obtained.

The percentage yield is given by this relationship:

$$\text{percentage yield} = \frac{\text{actual mass of product}}{\text{theoretical yield}} \times 100\%$$

Often one of the chemicals in a reaction mixture is present in an amount which limits the theoretical yield. The other reactants are added in excess to make sure that the most valuable chemical is converted as far as possible to the required product.

### Definition

The **limiting reactant** is the one that is not in excess and so is used up (if the reaction goes to completion).

## WORKED EXAMPLE

What is the theoretical yield of the ester ethyl ethanoate when 6.9 g ethanol reacts with excess ethanoic acid? What is the percentage yield if the actual yield of the ester in the laboratory is 8.6 g?

### Notes on the method

Start by writing the equation for the reaction. This need not be the full balanced equation so long as the equation includes the limiting reactant and the product.

Since the ethanoic anhydride is in excess the limiting reactant is the ethanol. This means that you can ignore the ethanoic acid during the calculation.

### Answer

The equation:

$$C_2H_5OH \xrightarrow{\text{heat with excess ethanoic acid and a drop of sulfuric acid}} CH_3CO_2C_2H_5$$
ethanol → ethyl ethanoate

1 mol of ethanol forms 1 mol of the ester.

The molar mass of ethanol, $C_2H_5OH = 46 \text{ g mol}^{-1}$

The amount of ethanol at the start of the synthesis

$$= \frac{6.9 \text{ g}}{46 \text{ g mol}^{-1}} = 0.15 \text{ mol}$$

The molar mass of the ester $= 88 \text{ g mol}^{-1}$

The theoretical yield of ester
$$= 0.15 \text{ mol} \times 88 \text{ g mol}^{-1}$$
$$= 13.2 \text{ g}$$

$$\text{Percentage yield} = \frac{8.6 \text{ g}}{13.2 \text{ g}} \times 100\% = 65\%$$

8  Strontium compounds can be made from the mineral celestite (strontium sulfate). A three stage process converts strontium sulfate, $SrSO_4(s)$, to strontium oxide, $SrO(s)$. Calculate the theoretical yield of strontium oxide from 9.2 g strontium sulfate.

9  A hot mixture of sodium bromide and concentrated sulfuric acid converts butan-1-ol, $C_4H_9OH(l)$, to 1-bromobutane, $C_4H_9Br(l)$.
   a  What is the theoretical yield of 1-bromobutane from 6.1 g butan-1-ol?
   b  What is the percentage yield if the actual yield is 6.8 g?

## Volumes of gases

### Avogadro's law

According to Avogadro's law, one mole of any gas occupies the same volume under the same conditions.

**Definition**

**Avogadro's law** states that equal volumes of gases under the same conditions of temperature and pressure contain equal numbers of molecules.

*The volume of a gas depends only on the amount of molecules (in moles) and not on the type of molecules.*

**Definition**

The **molar volume** of a gas is the volume of one mole of the gas under given conditions of temperature and pressure.

*Volume is the amount of space taken up by a sample. Chemists generally measure volumes in cubic decimetres, $dm^3$ (litres), or cubic centimetres, $cm^3$.*

The volume occupied by a gas at 273 K (0 °C) and 1 atmosphere pressure (100 kPa) is about 22.4 $dm^3$. These are the conditions of standard temperature and pressure (stp).

In a warmish laboratory at 298 K (25 °C) the volume of one mole of gas is about 24 $dm^3$ at 1 atmosphere pressure.

*Pressure is defined as force per unit area. The SI unit of pressure is the pascal (Pa) which is a pressure of one newton per square metre (1 N $m^{-2}$). The pascal is a very small unit so pressures are often quoted in kilopascals, kPa.*

### Reactions involving gases only

When gases are involved in reactions, the ratios of the volumes of gases are simple whole numbers, so long as all measurements are taken at the same temperature and pressure.

For example, 50 $cm^3$ nitrogen reacts with 150 $cm^3$ hydrogen to form 100 $cm^3$ of hydrogen chloride. The ratios are 1:3:2.

Avogadro's law accounts for these observations. If equal volumes of gases contains equal numbers of molecules, under the same conditions, it follows that the ratios of the volumes are also the ratios of the number of molecules as the equation shows.

$$N_2(g) + 3H_2(g) \rightarrow 2NH_3(g)$$
1 mol      3 mol      2 mol

*So, gas volume calculations are especially easy when the reactants and products involved are all gases.*

10  What volume of oxygen reacts with 20 $cm^3$ of propane gas, $C_3H_8(g)$, when it burns and what volume of carbon dioxide forms, if all gas volumes are measured at the same temperature and pressure?

11  When 100 $cm^3$ hydrogen chloride gas reacts with 80 $cm^3$ ammonia a white solid forms, $NH_4Cl(s)$, and there is an excess of one gas. Which gas is in excess and what volume of this gas remains unreacted?

### Reactions involving solids liquids and gases

Another approach to gas volume calculations applies when solids and liquids have to be taken into account as well as gases. The method is also based on Avogadro's law which states that the volume of a gas, under given conditions, depends only on the amount of gas in moles.

volume of gas/$cm^3$ = amount of gas/mol
$\times$ molar volume/$cm^3$ $mol^{-1}$

For making estimates under laboratory conditions the molar volume of a gas ≈ 24 000 cm³ at room temperature and pressure. So under laboratory conditions the volume of gas formed in a reaction can be estimated from this relationship:

volume of gas/cm³
= amount of gas/mol × 24 000 cm³ mol⁻¹

### WORKED EXAMPLE

What volume of hydrogen is produced under laboratory conditions when 0.35 g lithium reacts with excess water?

### Notes on the method

Start by writing the equation for the reaction. Convert the quantity of lithium to an amount in moles.

Use Avogadro's law to convert the amount of gas formed (in moles) to the volume.

### Answer

The equation for the reaction is:

$2Li(s) + 2H_2O(l) \rightarrow 2LiOH(aq) + H_2(g)$

The amount of lithium = 0.35 g ÷ 7 g mol⁻¹
= 0.05 mol

2 mol lithium produces 1 mol hydrogen.

So the amount of $H_2(g)$ formed = 0.025 mol

Volume of hydrogen = 0.025 mol × 24 000 cm³ mol⁻¹
= 600 cm³

### TEST YOURSELF

12 What volume of hydrogen forms under laboratory conditions when 1000 g of lithium hydride, LiH, reacts with water to form lithium hydroxide and hydrogen?

13 Marble chips, $CaCO_3$, react with dilute hydrochloric acid to form carbon dioxide gas. Calculate the mass of marble that must react to make 3 dm³ gas under laboratory conditions.

## Concentrations

Chemists measure the concentrations of solutions in moles per litre of solution (mol dm⁻³).

$$concentration/mol\ dm^{-3} = \frac{amount\ of\ solute/mol}{volume\ of\ solution/dm^3}$$

ℹ There are small volume changes when chemicals dissolve in water so it is important to note that concentrations normally refer to litres of solution not to litres of the solvent.

This rearranges to give:

amount of solute/mol
= volume of solution/dm³ × concentration/mol dm⁻³

ℹ Note that the units must be consistent. The volume of solution in these relationships is in dm³.

### WORKED EXAMPLE

What is the concentration of a solution of sodium hydroxide made by dissolving 5.00 g of the solid in water and making the solution up to 500 cm³?

### Note on the method

Remember to convert volumes in cm³ to volumes in dm³ before substituting in the relationships.

### Answer

The molar mass of sodium hydroxide, NaOH = 40 g mol⁻¹

Amount of NaOH in solution $= \dfrac{5.00\ g}{40\ g\ mol^{-1}}$
= 0.125 mol

Volume of the solution $= \dfrac{500}{1000}\ dm^3 = 0.5\ dm^3$

Concentration $= \dfrac{0.125\ mol}{0.5\ dm^3} = 0.25\ mol\ dm^{-3}$

### TEST YOURSELF

14 What is the concentration of the following solutions:
a 0.002 mol ammonia, $NH_3$, in 20 cm³ solution?
b 4.25 g silver nitrate, $AgNO_3$, in 500 cm³ solution?
c 5.6 g potassium hydroxide, KOH, in 250 cm³ solution?

15 What amount, in moles, of the named substance is there in the following:
   a  25 cm³ of 0.5 mol dm⁻³ potassium iodide solution?
   b  100 cm³ of 2.0 mol dm⁻³ dilute nitric acid?
   c  2 dm³ of 0.001 mol dm⁻³ ammonia solution?

Calculations from equations that involve solutions are carried out in a similar way to calculations involving the masses of solids and liquids or the volumes of gases.

### WORKED EXAMPLE

What is the mass of silver bromide that precipitates on adding excess sodium bromide solution to 10 cm³ of 0.5 mol dm⁻³ silver nitrate solution?

### Answer

$AgNO_3(aq) + NaBr(aq) \longrightarrow AgBr(s) + NaNO_3(aq)$

The sodium bromide is in excess so the limiting reagent is the silver nitrate. The equation shows that 1 mol $AgNO_3(aq)$ produces 1 mol $AgBr(s)$.

The molar mass of silver bromide
$$= 108 \text{ g mol}^{-1} + 80 \text{ g mol}^{-1}$$
$$= 188 \text{ g mol}^{-1}$$

So 1 mol $AgNO_3(aq)$ produces 188 g $AgBr(s)$
The amount of $AgNO_3$ in solution

$$= \frac{10}{1000} \text{ dm}^3 \times 0.5 \text{ mol dm}^{-3}$$

$$= 0.005 \text{ mol}$$

Therefore the mass of $AgBr(s)$ that precipitates
$$= 0.005 \times 188 \text{ g}$$
$$= 0.94 \text{ g}$$

16 Calculate the mass of barium sulfate, BaSO₄, that precipitates on adding excess sodium sulfate, Na₂SO₄, solution to 10 cm³ of 0.5 mol dm⁻³ barium nitrate solution.

17 Calculate the volume of gas under laboratory conditions produced when excess magnesium reacts completely with 50 cm³ of 1.0 mol dm⁻³ dilute hydrochloric acid.

18 Calculate the volume of 2.0 mol dm⁻³ dilute nitric acid that is neutralised by 1.4 g calcium oxide, CaO.

## Acid-base titrations

Chemists use titrations to investigate reactions and to analyse solutions. A titration involves two solutions. When you do an acid-base titration you measure one solution into a flask with a pipette. You add an indicator and then add the second solution bit by bit from a burette until the reaction is complete.

### Definition

The **end-point** of a titration is the point at which a colour change shows that the volume of solution from the burette is just enough to react with all of the chemical in the flask.

Figure 02.02 shows the apparatus for a titration involving a solution A which reacts with solution B. Suppose the equation for the reaction takes the form:

$$n_A A + n_B B \rightarrow \text{products}$$

which means that $n_A$ moles of A reacts with $n_B$ moles of B.

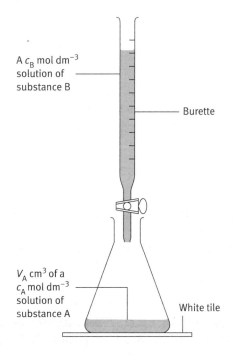

A $c_B$ mol dm⁻³ solution of substance B

Burette

$V_A$ cm³ of a $c_A$ mol dm⁻³ solution of substance A

White tile

**02.02  Titration apparatus**

In the laboratory, volumes of solutions are normally measured in cm³ but they should be converted to dm³ in calculations so that they are consistent with the units used to measure concentrations (1 dm³ = 1000 cm³).

The concentration of A in the flask is $c_A$ mol dm⁻³ and its volume is $V_A$ dm³.

The concentration of B in the burette is $c_B$ mol dm⁻³. $V_B$ dm³ of solution B is added until the indicator shows that the end-point has been reached.

The amount of A in the flask at the start = $V_A \times c_A$ mol

The amount of B added from the burette = $V_B \times c_B$ mol

The ratio of these amounts must be the same as the ratio of the amounts shown in the equation.

$$\frac{V_A \times c_A}{V_B \times c_B} = \frac{n_A}{n_B}$$

> **i** *In any titration all but one of the values in this formula are known. The one unknown is determined from the results.*

### Definition

A **standard solution** is a solution with an accurately known concentration.

### TEST YOURSELF

19 A 100 cm³ sample of concentrated hydrochloric acid was diluted to 1000 cm³ with water. 10 cm³ of the diluted solution reacted exactly with 20 cm³ of 0.1 mol dm⁻³ sodium hydroxide. What was the concentration of the undiluted acid?

20 A 1.575 g sample of ethanedioic acid crystals, $H_2C_2O_4.nH_2O$ was dissolved in water and made up to 250 cm³. One mole of the acid is neutralised by two moles of sodium hydroxide. In a titration, 25.0 cm³ of the solution of the acid reacted with 15.6 cm³ of 0.16 mol dm⁻³ sodium hydroxide solution.
   a Calculate the concentration of the acid in mol dm⁻³.
   b Hence work out the mass of one mole of the acid.
   c Deduce the value of $n$.

### REVIEW

Go through this section and pick out all the relationships used in the calculations. Add the relationships to the appropriate place on your Mind Map.

Solving the 'test yourself' problems is the most effective way of revising the ideas in this topic. Check your answers against the solutions on page 170. Where you feel the need for more practice, look for more examples in past examination papers and text books.

### WORKED EXAMPLE

A 2.65 g sample of anhydrous sodium carbonate was dissolved in water and the solution made up to 250 cm³. In a titration, 25.0 cm³ of this solution required 22.5 cm³ of hydrochloric acid at the end-point with methyl orange as the indicator. Calculate the concentration of the acid.

### Notes on the method

Always start by writing the equation for the reaction.

Remember to convert volumes in cm³ to volumes in dm³ by dividing by 1000.

In any titration there is one unknown – in this case the concentration of the acid, $c_B$.

### Answer

The equation for the reaction is:

$Na_2CO_3(aq) + 2HCl(aq)$
$\rightarrow 2NaCl(aq) + H_2O(l) + CO_2(g)$

The molar mass of $Na_2CO_3$ = 106 g mol⁻¹

So (2.65 g ÷ 106 g mol⁻¹) = 0.025 mol $Na_2CO_3$ was dissolved in 250 cm³ = 0.25 dm³ of the solution

The concentration of the solution in the flask, $c_A$ = (0.025 mol ÷ 0.25 dm³) = 0.1 mol dm⁻³

The volume of sodium carbonate solution in the flask, $V_A = \dfrac{25.0}{1000}$ dm³

The volume of hydrochloric acid added from the burette, $V_B = \dfrac{22.5}{1000}$ dm³

Let the concentration of hydrochloric acid be $c_B$.

$$\frac{V_A \times c_A}{V_B \times c_B} = \frac{n_A}{n_B}$$

$$\frac{\left(\dfrac{25.0 \times 0.1}{1000}\right)}{\left(\dfrac{22.5 \times c_B}{1000}\right)} = \frac{1}{2}$$

Therefore $c_B = \dfrac{2 \times 25.0 \times 0.1}{22.5} = 0.22$ mol dm⁻³

The concentration of the hydrochloric acid was 0.22 mol dm⁻³.

By the end of this topic you will be able to:

✔ **explain the behaviour of solids, liquids and gases in terms of the movement of particles (atoms, molecules and ions) and the forces between them**

✔ **account for the energy changes during changes of state**

✔ **understand that the ideal gas equation closely describes the behaviour of many gases**

✔ **describe the three types of strong chemical bonding (metallic, covalent and ionic) in terms of the sharing or transfer of electrons**

✔ **recognise when it is likely that the bonding in a compound will be intermediate between ionic and covalent**

✔ **distinguish between giant and molecular structures and be able to describe examples of these structures**

✔ **predict the shapes of molecules**

✔ **account for the relatively weak forces between molecules and know when hydrogen bonding between molecules will affect the properties of a compound**

✔ **interpret the physical properties of elements and compounds in terms of structure and bonding.**

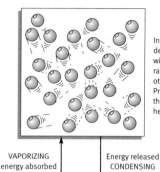

In a gas the particles are spread out, so the densities of gas are very low compared with solids and liquids. The particles move rapidly in a random manner, colliding with other particles and the vessel's walls. Pressure is caused by the particles hitting the walls. Light particles move faster than heavier ones.

VAPORIZING energy absorbed     Energy released CONDENSING

The particles in a liquid are closely packed but are free to move around, sliding past each other

MELTING energy absorbed     Energy released FREEZING

Particles in a solid are packed close together in a regular way. The particles do not move freely, but vibrate in their positions.

**03.01 Energy changes and changes of state**

## States of matter

### Changes of state

Solids and liquids can only exist because there are attractive forces between atoms in elements and compounds. Some materials have high melting and boiling points because all the forces between the particles are strong. Where some of the interparticle forces are weak, the materials have low melting and boiling points.

> ℹ️ *Energy is needed to break bonds – so energy has to be supplied to melt a solid and then vaporise the liquid.*

> ℹ️ *Energy is given out when bonds form – so energy has to be removed from a gas to make it condense and then to freeze the liquid.*

## TEST YOURSELF

1 **Explain what is happening at each stage (from one letter to the next) in Figure 03.02.**

2 **How would the graph in Figure 03.02 differ if the substance were impure?**

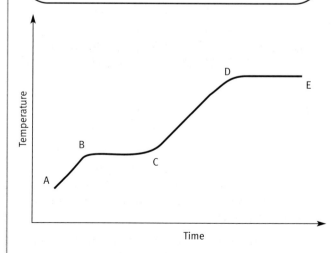

**03.02 The temperature changes on heating a pure substance**

## Ideal and real gases

For any sample of gas you can define its:

- pressure, *p*,
- volume, *V*,
- temperature, *T*, and its
- amount, n (in moles).

The behaviour of gases such as helium, hydrogen and oxygen at room temperature is summed up in the ideal gas equation.

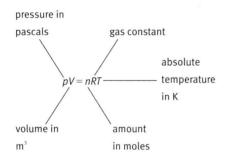

**03.03 The ideal gas equation. Always convert to SI units before substituting in this equation**

### Definitions

An **ideal gas** is an imaginary gas that obeys the ideal gas equation perfectly. **Real gases** deviate to some extent from ideal gas behaviour. It is the gases that can easily be liquefied by cooling or increasing the pressure, such as butane or ammonia, which deviate markedly from ideal behaviour.

### Definitions

**Vapours** are gases formed by evaporation of substances that are usually liquids or solids at room temperature. So chemists talk about oxygen gas but water vapour. Vapours are easily condensed by cooling or increasing the pressure.

A liquid **boils** when it is hot enough for bubbles of vapour to form within the body of the liquid. This happens when the pressure of the vapour escaping from the liquid equals the outside pressure. The **boiling point** of a liquid is its boiling temperature at normal atmospheric pressure.

If the volume, *V*, of a gas, and the amount, *n*, are both constant, then the pressure, *p*, of the gas is proportional to the temperature, *T*, on the Kelvin scale. This defines the Kelvin scale of temperature as shown in Figure 03.04.

Chemists use the ideal gas equation to measure the molar masses of gases or of liquids that vaporise easily.

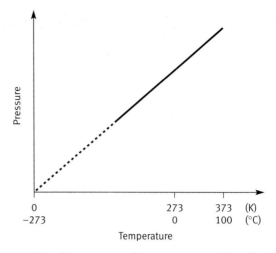

**03.04 Plot of pressure against temperature for a fixed amount of an ideal gas at a constant volume**

### WORKED EXAMPLE

A 0.125 g sample of an alcohol was injected into a syringe which was then heated in a water bath at 100 °C. Once the vapour stopped expanding its volume was 85 cm³ when the pressure was 100 kPa. What was the molar mass of the alcohol?

#### Notes on the method

Use the ideal gas equation to find the amount in moles, *n* (the only unknown). Then you know both the mass in grams and the amount in moles making it possible to calculate the molar mass.

Convert all the quantities to SI units before substituting in the ideal gas equation. Volume: $1\ cm^3 = 10^{-6}\ m^3$. Pressure: $1\ kPa = 1000\ Pa$. Temperature in K = temperature in °C + 273.

The ideal gas constant $R = 8.314\ J\ K^{-1}\ mol^{-1}$

#### Answer

$$n = \frac{PV}{RT} = \frac{100\ 000\ Pa \times 85 \times 10^{-6}\ m^3}{8.314\ J\ K^{-1}\ mol^{-1} \times 373\ K}$$

$$= 2.74 \times 10^{-3}\ mol$$

Molar mass $= 0.125\ g \div 2.74 \times 10^{-3}\ mol$
$\qquad\qquad = 45.6\ g\ mol^{-1}$

The measurement of volume is only accurate to two significant figures. Also the alcohol vapour is not a perfectly ideal gas. So the result shows that the molar mass is about 46 g mol⁻¹.

### TEST YOURSELF

3 **A 0.160 g sample of a hydrocarbon was injected into a gas syringe and heated to 80 °C. The volume of vapour formed was 80 cm³. The pressure was 100 600 Pa. What was the molar mass of the hydrocarbon?**

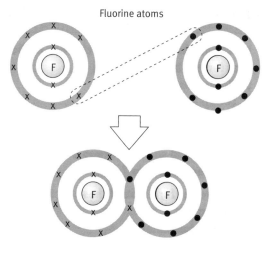

Fluorine atoms

Fluorine molecule

**03.12 Covalent bonding in a fluorine molecule**

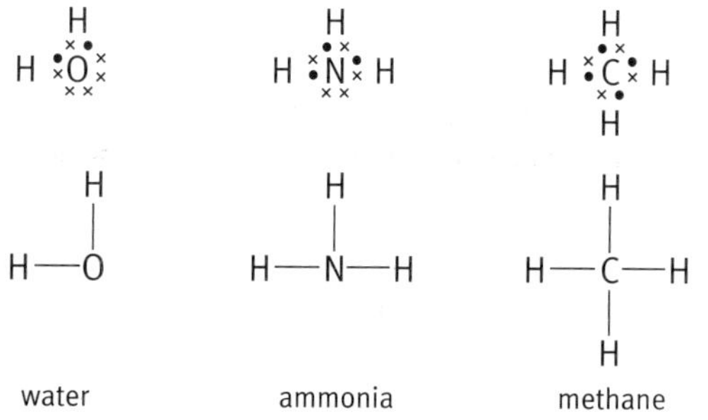

water          ammonia          methane

**03.13 Covalent bonding in water, ammonia and methane molecules. Note that water and ammonia molecules have lone pairs of electrons. Lone pairs are electron pairs in the outer shells of atoms in a molecule or ion which are not involved in bonding**

### Factfile

**Numbers of colavent bonds formed by atoms**

| Element | Number of bonds |
| --- | --- |
| hydrogen | 1 |
| oxygen | 2 |
| nitrogen | 3 |
| carbon | 4 |
| halogens (F, Cl, Br, I) | 1 |

## Multiple covalent bonding

One shared pair of electrons makes a single bond. Double or triple bonds are also possible with two or three shared pairs of electrons.

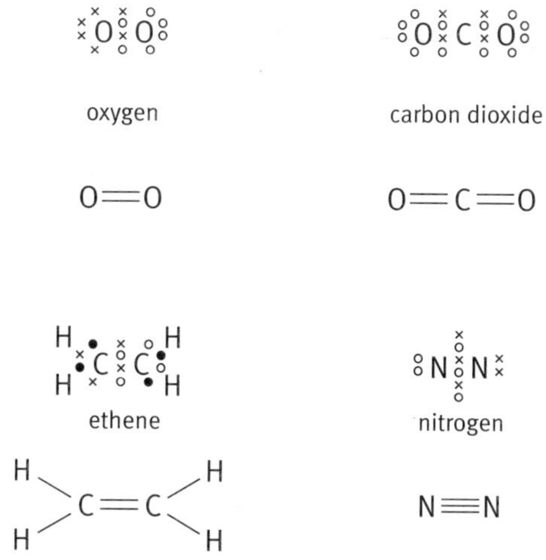

oxygen          carbon dioxide

O=O          O=C=O

ethene          nitrogen

N≡N

**03.14 Dot-and-cross diagrams showing double and triple bonding. Note that, by sharing electrons, each atom ends up with an outer shell electron configuration the same as the nearest noble gas**

## Dative covalent bonding

Sometimes one atom supplies the electrons needed to make a covalent bond. Chemists call this dative covalent bonding.

> **i** *Dative* means 'giving' – in a dative bond one atom gives both the electrons to the bond.

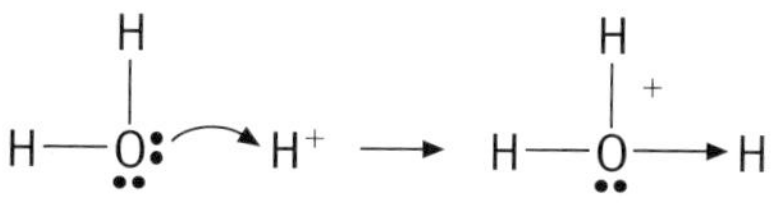

**03.15 Oxygen in a water molecule forming a dative bond with a hydrogen ion**

> **i** *Once formed there is no difference between a dative bond and any other covalent bond.*

Dative bonds also form between molecules or ions with lone pairs and metals ions. The resulting ions are quite complicated, as Figure 03.16 shows, so chemists call them complex ions.

Chemists also have a special name for compounds in which metal ions have other molecules or ions clustered around them to make complex ions. They call them co-ordination compounds. So an alternative name for dative covalent bonding is co-ordinate bonding.

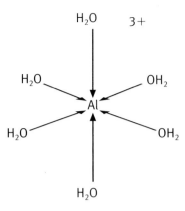

**03.16 Dative bonding in a hydrated aluminium ion – a complex ion**

---

**TEST YOURSELF**

10 Draw dot-and-cross diagrams to show the covalent bonding in:
   a bromine
   b hydrogen chloride
   c hydrogen sulfide
   d carbon disulfide.

11 Draw a diagram to show dative bonding:
   a when an ammonia molecule combines with a hydrogen ion
   b in a hydrated magnesium ion with six water molecules linked to the metal atom.

---

## Shapes of molecules

You can predict the shape of a molecule by counting up the number of electron pairs around the central atom. The electron pairs repel each other so that molecules take up shapes which keep these electron pairs as far apart as possible in three dimensions.

All electron pairs count, both bonding pairs and lone pairs. Lone pairs are held closer to the central atom. The result is that the order of repulsion is:

lone pair–lone pair > lone pair–bond pair > bond pair–bond pair

> ℹ *Remember that it is only the electron pairs around the atom in the middle that determine the shape of a molecule.*

A double bond counts as one region when it comes to predicting molecular shapes. The same is true for a triple bond.

---

**TEST YOURSELF**

12 Predict the shapes of these molecules and ions: $PH_3$, $NH_2^-$, $CO_2$, $CH_3$—$CH$=$CH_2$, $BCl_3$.

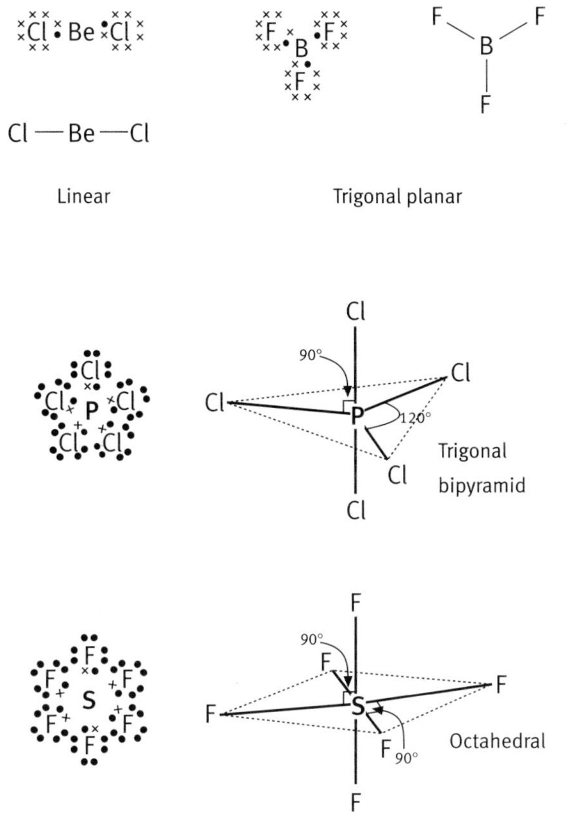

---

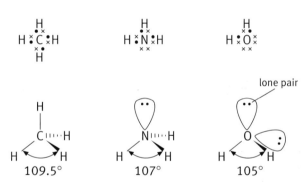

**03.17 Shapes of molecules with 2, 3, 5 and 6 electrons around the central atom**

**03.18 Shapes of molecules with lone pairs of electrons. Note the effect of lone pairs on the bond angles**

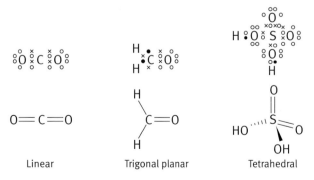

**03.19 Shapes of molecules with double bonds**

The same rules apply when it comes to predicting the shapes of ions which consist of more than one atom.

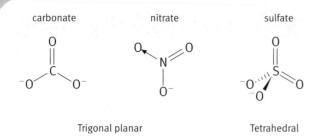

carbonate      nitrate      sulfate

Trigonal planar      Tetrahedral

**03.20 Shapes of ions consisting of more than one atom**

### Polar covalent bonds

If the two atoms joined by the bond are not the same, then the electron pair in the covalent bond is not shared equally. One atom attracts the electrons more strongly than the other. This means that one end of the bond has a slight excess of negative charge ($\delta-$). The other end of the bond has a slight deficit of electrons so that the charge cloud of electrons does not cancel the positive charge on the nucleus ($\delta+$).

**03.21 A polar covalent bond in hydrogen chloride**

> **i** *Chemists use the symbol $\delta$ (a Greek delta) for a small quantity or change. They use the symbols $\delta+$ and $\delta-$ for the small charges at the ends of a polar bond.*

**Definition**

The **electronegativity** of an element measures the power of its atoms to attract electrons when bonded to other atoms. The stronger the pulling power of an atom, the higher its electronegativity.

The highly electronegative elements, such as fluorine and oxygen, are at the top right of the periodic table. The least electronegative elements, such as caesium, are at the bottom left.

The bigger the difference in the electronegativity of the elements forming a bond, the more polar the bond. Oxygen is more electronegative than hydrogen, so an O—H bond is polar with a slight negative charge on the oxygen atoms and a slight positive charge on the hydrogen atom.

**03.22 Examples of polar bonds between atoms with different electronegativities**

Molecules with polar bonds may or may not be polar. It depends on the number of bonds and the way they are arranged.

Overall polar      Overall non-polar

**03.23 Molecules with polar bonds. Note that in the examples on the left the net effect of all the bonds is a polar molecule. In the examples on the right the overall effect is a non-polar molecule**

**Definition**

A **polar molecule** has a positive end (pole) and a negative end (pole). So it is an electrical **dipole**.

**TEST YOURSELF**

13 Draw the structures of these molecules and use the symbols $\delta+$ and $\delta-$ to label the polar bonds. Which of the following molecules are overall polar and which are non-polar?

$CH_2Cl_2$, $CCl_4$, $H_2S$, $CH_3Br$, $HCHO$, $SO_2$.

## Intermolecular forces

Intermolecular forces are weak attractive forces between molecules. Without intermolecular forces there could be no molecular liquids or solids.

Weak intermolecular forces arise from the electrostatic attraction between dipoles. The attraction can be between:

- permanent dipoles in polar molecules
- temporary dipoles in non-polar molecules.

Chemists often call these weak intermolecular forces 'van der Waals' forces' after the Dutch scientist who used the idea of intermolecular forces to explain why the behaviour of real gases deviates from the ideal gas equation.

### Permanent dipole–permanent dipole

Molecules with permanent dipoles attract each other. The positive end of one molecule tends to attract the negative end of another.

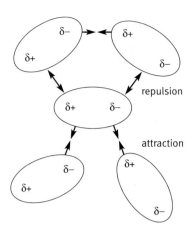

**03.24 Attractions between molecules with permanent dipoles**

## Temporary dipole–temporary dipole

Why do non-polar molecules attract each other? It turns out that when non-polar atoms or molecules meet there are fleeting repulsions and attractions between the nuclei of the atoms and the surrounding clouds of electrons. Temporary displacements of the electrons lead to temporary dipoles. These instantaneous dipoles can induce dipoles in neighbouring molecules.

The weakest intermolecular forces are the attractions between these instantaneous and induced dipoles, which give rise to the tendency for the molecules to stick together. Forces of this kind are roughly a hundred times weaker than covalent bonds.

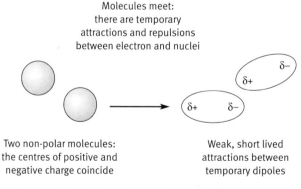

Molecules meet:
there are temporary
attractions and repulsions
between electron and nuclei

Two non-polar molecules:
the centres of positive and
negative charge coincide

Weak, short lived
attractions between
temporary dipoles

**03.25 The origins of temporary induced dipoles**

The greater the number of electrons, the greater the polarisability of the molecule and the greater the possibility for temporary, induced dipoles. This explains why the boiling points rise down Group 7 (the halogens) and Group 8 (the noble gases).

**Definition**

The **polarisablity** of a molecule shows how easily the electron cloud in the molecule is distorted by a nearby electric charge. Larger molecules with more electrons are usually more polarisable.

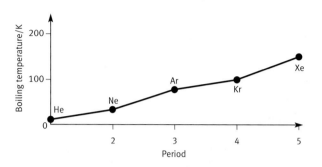

**03.26 The trend in the boiling points of the noble gases with increasing atomic number**

Longer molecules tend to have greater intermolecular forces than shorter, more compact molecules because there is a greater surface area over which the forces can act.

So the boiling points in alkanes increase with the increasing number of carbon atoms in these hydrocarbon molecules.

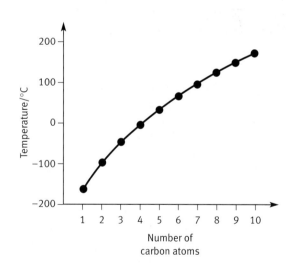

**03.27 Plot showing how the boiling points of straight-chain alkanes increase as the chains get longer**

## Hydrogen bonding

Hydrogen bonding is a type of attraction between molecules that is about ten times stronger than other types of intermolecular force, but still at least ten times weaker than covalent bonding.

In a hydrogen bond the hydrogen atom lies between two highly electronegative atoms (fluorine, oxygen or nitrogen). It is hydrogen bonded to one of them and covalently bonded to the other. The covalent bond is highly polar.

The small hydrogen atom ($\delta+$), which has no inner shells of electrons to shield its nucleus, can get close to the other electronegative atom ($\delta-$) to which it is strongly attracted.

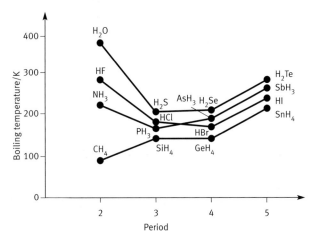

hydrogen bond

covalent bond

**03.28    Hydrogen bonding in hydrogen fluoride**

> **i** *The three atoms associated with a hydrogen bond are always in a straight line: Y⋯H—X (where are Y and X are the electronegative atoms F, O or N).*

Hydrogen bonding accounts for the relatively high boiling points of ammonia, water and hydrogen fluoride, which are out of line for the trends in the properties of the other hydrides in Groups 5, 6 and 7.

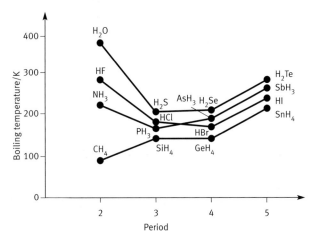

**03.29    Boiling points for the hydrides of the elements in Groups 4, 5, 6 and 7. Note that methane is not affected by hydrogen bonding**

## Structures based on covalent bonding

### Covalent molecular structures

The covalent bonds holding the atoms together in molecules are strong so the molecules do not easily break up into atoms. The intermolecular forces (see page 24) are weak so that it is quite easy to separate

---

> **T E S T   Y O U R S E L F**
>
> **14** Identify the main type of intermolecular force in these molecules: HI, $C_4H_{10}$, $C_2H_5OH$.
>
> **15** Why is methanol, $CH_3OH$, a liquid at room temperature while propane, $C_3H_8$, is a gas?
>
> **16** Draw diagrams to illustrate hydrogen bonding:
>
>   **a** in liquid ammonia
>
>   **b** in a solution of ammonia in water.
>
> **17** Explain the trend in boiling points in the series: HCl, HBr, HI (see Figure 03.29). Why is HF out of line with the trend?
>
> **18** Ethene is a gas at room temperature. The long chain polymer, polyethene, is a solid. How do you account for this difference?
>
> **19** Why is the boiling point of 2,2-dimethylpropane lower than the boiling point of its isomer butane?

them. This means that molecular substances are often liquids or gases at room temperature. Molecular solids are typically easy to melt or evaporate. Iodine and ice are examples.

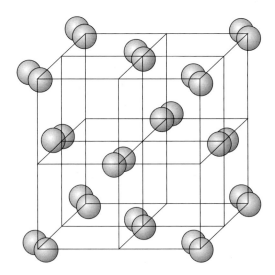

**03.30    Structure of iodine showing the arrangement of iodine molecules**

Figure 03.29 shows that water would be a gas well below room temperature if it behaved like the other hydrides in Group 6. Thanks to hydrogen bonding water is a liquid under normal conditions and freezes at only a little below room temperature.

Study and Revise AS and A2 Level Chemistry

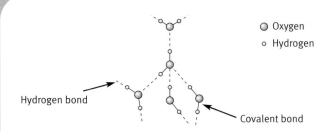

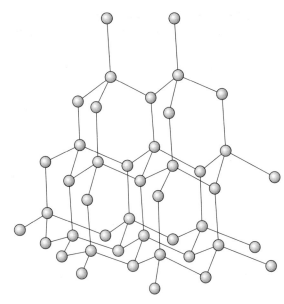

**03.31 Molecules in ice held together by hydrogen bonding**

The hydrogen bonds hold water molecules in a very open structure so that ice is less dense than water at 0 °C. As a result, ice floats on water.

**03.32 Fragment of a diamond giant structure**

conducts electricity. The bonding between the layers is weak making graphite useful as a lubricant as the layers can slide over each other.

### Factfile

**Covalent molecular structures**

| Property | Explanation |
|---|---|
| * Low melting and boiling points | The forces between the molecules are weak |
| * Non-conductors of electricity when solid and when liquid | Molecules are uncharged. There are no free electrons. No charge carriers |
| * Insoluble in water but soluble in organic solvents if non-polar | Non-polar molecules cannot break into the hydrogen-bonded structure of water but can mix freely with other non-polar molecules |
| * Soluble in water if highly polar or with atoms that can form hydrogen bonds | Molecules with oxygen or nitrogen atoms such as alcohols and amines can form hydrogen bonds with water molecules |

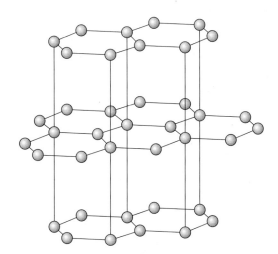

**03.33 Fragment of a graphite giant structure**

Silicon oxide is a compound with a covalent giant structure. The mineral silica in sand consists mainly of silicon dioxide.

### Covalent giant structures

In some non-metal elements and compounds the covalent bond is continuous throughout the structure. Diamond and graphite are forms of carbon with giant covalent structures. Substances with this kind of structure have very high melting points.

Graphite also has a giant structure with a high melting point. Every atom in a layer of this structure contributes one electron to a cloud of delocalised electrons that are free to move. Therefore graphite

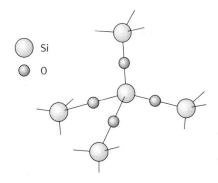

**03.34 Fragment of the giant structure of silicon dioxide**

## Factfile

### Covalent giant structures

| Property | Explanation |
| --- | --- |
| * High melting and boiling points | The network of strong bonding is continuous with with no weak links |
| * Hard and strong | Covalent bonds are strong and have a definite length and direction. In a giant structure there are no weak links |
| * Normally non-conductors of electricity | In most covalent bonds the electrons are fixed and cannot move. An exception is graphite which has delocalised electrons |
| * Insoluble in water and organic solvents | Solvent molecules cannot bond with the non-metal atoms strongly enough to break up the giant structure |

## TEST YOURSELF

**20** Carbon dioxide and silicon dioxide are both oxides of Group 4 elements. Why is one a gas while the other is a solid with a very high melting point?

**21** Which of these non-metal elements are molecular and which have giant structures? Carbon, nitrogen, silicon, sulfur, chlorine, bromine.

## In-between types of bonding

In a compound between a reactive metal such as potassium and the most reactive non-metal, fluorine, the bonding is definitely ionic.

In a molecule such as bromine where both atoms are the same, the electrons are equally shared and the bonding is purely covalent.

In most compounds between different elements, the bonding is neither purely ionic nor purely covalent but somewhere in between.

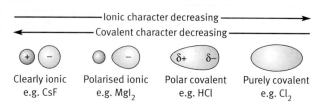

| Ionic character decreasing → |
| ← Covalent character decreasing |

Clearly ionic e.g. CsF | Polarised ionic e.g. $MgI_2$ | Polar covalent e.g. HCl | Purely covalent e.g. $Cl_2$

### 03.35 A spectrum of bonding

Turn to Section 3.5 for an explanation of how chemists use electronegativity values to predict the polarity of covalent bonds.

Starting at the other end of the spectrum of bonding, chemists start by picturing purely ionic bonding between two atoms. They then consider the extent to which the positive metal ion will distort the neighbouring negative ions giving rise to some degree of electron sharing (that is a degree of covalent bonding).

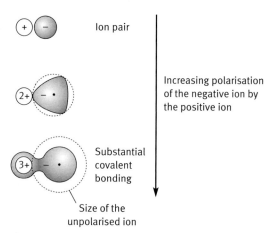

Ion pair

Increasing polarisation of the negative ion by the positive ion

Substantial covalent bonding

Size of the unpolarised ion

**03.36 Ionic bonding with increasing degrees of electron sharing because the positive ion has distorted the neighbouring negative ion. Dotted circles show the unpolarised ions**

A spherical anion is non-polar. When a positive ion pulls the electron cloud towards itself it turns the negative ion into a little dipole (with a positive pole and a negative pole). So chemists say that the positive ion polarises the negative ion.

The smaller a positive ion and the larger its charge, the greater the extent to which it tends to polarise a negative ion.

Polarising power increases along the series, $Na^+$, $Mg^{2+}$, $Al^{3+}$, $Si^{4+}$, as the ions get smaller and more highly charged.

The larger the negative ion and the larger its charge, the more polarisable it becomes. So iodide ions are more polarisable than fluoride ions. Fluorine, which forms the small, singly charged fluoride ion, forms more ionic compounds than any other non-metal. Sulfide ions, $S^{2-}$, are more polarisable than chloride ions, $Cl^-$.

### TEST YOURSELF

**22** Classify the bonding in the following compounds under these headings: covalent, polar covalent, ionic with some covalent character, ionic.

Sodium chloride, magnesium chloride, aluminium chloride, silicon tetrachloride, lithium fluoride, magnesium sulfide, methane, fluorine.

### REVIEW

✔ Draw your own colourful Mind Map to summarise what you know about structure and bonding. You can use Figure 03.37 as a starting point if you wish.

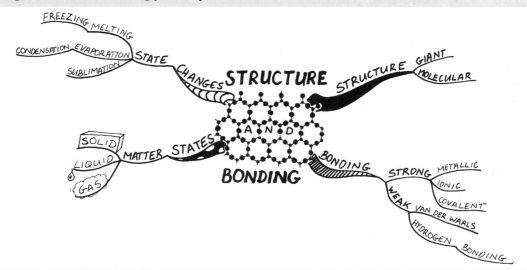

**03.37**

✔ **What type of strong bonding would you expect in these substances?** Carbon dioxide, magnesium oxide, calcium, chlorine, lithium fluoride, aluminium, ammonia, diamond.

✔ **Make a table to sum up what you know about the properties of materials with different types of structure. The columns headings might be:**

- **type of structure**

- **boiling point – reason**

- **electrical conductivity – reason**

- **solubility in water/organic solvents – reason.**

✔ **Use a book of data to test the key in Figure 03.38. Can you find any substances that break the rules in the key?**

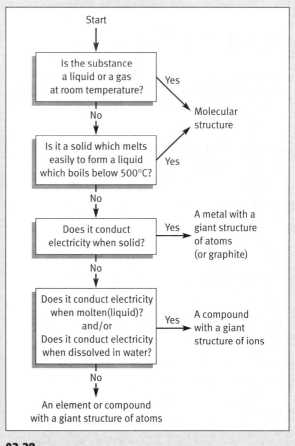

**03.38**

**By the end of this topic you will be able to:**

✔ understand that enthalpy changes, $\Delta H$, are measured under constant pressure and are negative for exothermic reactions and positive for endothermic reactions

✔ draw and interpret enthalpy level diagrams

✔ calculate the enthalpy change for a reaction from measurements taken with a calorimeter

✔ recognise the conditions used to define standard enthalpy changes, $\Delta H^{\ominus}$

✔ define $\Delta H^{\ominus}_{c}$, $\Delta H^{\ominus}_{f}$, $\Delta H^{\ominus}_{neutralisation}$

✔ apply Hess's law to calculate enthalpy changes

✔ determine mean bond enthalpies from data and use them to calculate the value of $\Delta H$ for reactions

✔ recognise that the sign of $\Delta H$ often indicates the direction of spontaneous change but that there are exceptions to the general rule.

## Enthalpy changes

Chemists usually work with chemicals in open containers so they measure energy changes at constant pressure.

**Definitions**

The term **system** describes the material or mixture of chemicals being studied. Everything around the system is the **surroundings**, such as the apparatus, the air in the laboratory – in theory, everything else in the universe.

When there is a change in an open system some energy is almost always transferred between the system and its surroundings. The **enthalpy change** is the energy transferred between the system and its surroundings when the change happens at constant pressure.

The symbol for an enthalpy change is $\Delta H$ and the units are kJ mol$^{-1}$.

## Exothermic reactions

Exothermic changes give out energy to their surroundings. Burning is an exothermic chemical reaction and so is respiration.

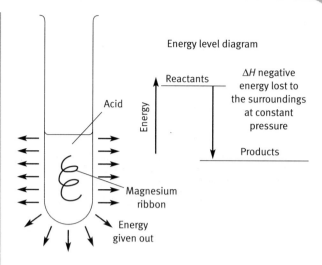

**04.01 An exothermic reaction**

An energy level diagram shows that after an exothermic reaction the system has less energy than it did at the start. So for an exothermic reaction the enthalpy change, $\Delta H$, is negative.

> **i** *In an **ex**othermic change, energy leaves the system – just as people leave a building by the **ex**it.*

## Endothermic reactions

Endothermic changes take in energy from their surroundings. Photosynthesis is endothermic as plants take in energy from the sun.

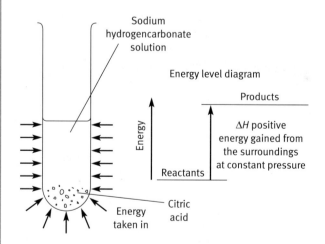

**04.02 An endothermic reaction**

An energy level diagram shows that after an endothermic reaction the system has more energy than it did at the start. So for an endothermic reaction the enthalpy change, $\Delta H$, is positive.

# Calorimetry

### Measuring enthalpies of combustion

The easiest way to measure the enthalpy of combustion of a fuel is to burn a measured mass of fuel in such a way that the energy heats a calorimeter containing water. Measuring the temperature rise of the water makes it possible to calculate the quantity of energy transferred from the flame to the water.

### Definition

A **calorimeter** is an apparatus for measuring the energy change during a chemical reaction. Typically a calorimeter is insulated from its surroundings and contains water. The energy from the reaction heats up the water and the rest of the apparatus. An accurate thermometer measures the temperature rise.

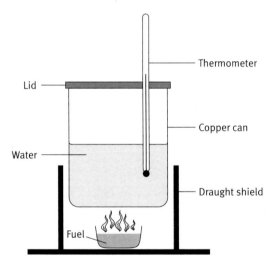

**04.03  An approximate method for measuring the enthalpy of combustion of a fuel**

### Definition

The **specific heat capacity** of a material, $c$, is the energy needed to raise the temperature of 1 g of the material by 1 K. The specific heat capacity of water is given by $c = 4.2 \text{ J g}^{-1} \text{ K}^{-1}$. So it takes 4.2 joules of energy to raise the temperature of one gram of water by one degree. The energy, $q$, needed to raise the temperature of a mass of water, $m$, through a temperature change $\Delta T$ is given by: $q = mc\Delta T$.

> **i** *A temperature change of 1 °C is the same as a temperature change of 1 K. Always use Kelvin degrees in calculations.*

### WORKED EXAMPLE

When 0.92 g ethanol, $C_2H_5OH$, was burnt in the apparatus shown in Figure 04.03 the temperature of 250 g water in the copper can rose from 20.0 °C to 39.5 °C. What is the enthalpy of combustion of ethanol?

### Notes on the method

Ignore the heat capacity of the copper can because it is small and other sources of error are larger.

Work with temperatures and temperature changes in Kelvin. The magnitude of the temperature rise is the same on the Celsius and Kelvin scales (see Figure 03.04).

Energy     = mass of × temperature × specific
transferred/J   water/g      rise/K        heat
                                         capacity/
                                         J mol$^{-1}$ K$^{-1}$

### Answer

Temperature rise of the water = 19.5 K

Energy transferred to the water
$$= 250 \text{ g} \times 19.5 \text{ K} \times 4.2 \text{ J mol}^{-1} \text{ K}^{-1}$$
$$= 20\,475 \text{ J} = 20.5 \text{ kJ}$$

Molar mass of ethanol (see page 8)
$$= 46 \text{ g mol}^{-1}$$

Amount of ethanol burnt
$$= 0.92 \text{ g} \div 46 \text{ g mol}^{-1}$$
$$= 0.02 \text{ mol}$$

Energy from burning one mole ethanol
$$= 20.5 \text{ kJ} \div 0.02 \text{ mol}$$
$$= 1025 \text{ kJ mol}^{-1}$$

Combustion is exothermic so the enthalpy change is negative.

$\Delta H_{\text{combustion}} = -1025 \text{ kJ mol}^{-1}$

This method of working wrongly assumes that all the energy from the flame heats the water. In practice a proportion of the energy heats the air and surrounding equipment.

### TEST YOURSELF

1  **Burning 1.2 g butanone, $CH_3CH_2COCH_3$, under a can of water raised the temperature of 500 g water from 15.0 °C to 30.4 °C. Estimate the molar enthalpy change of combustion of butanone.**

## Where does the energy come from?

During combustion the bonds in the fuel and oxygen break and new bonds form to make new molecules. Energy is needed to break bonds. Energy is released as bonds form.

 *Bond breaking is endothermic.*

 *Bond forming is exothermic.*

Each type of bond in a molecule has its own 'bond enthalpy' (see Section 4.5). When hydrogen burns in oxygen:

$$2H_2(g) + O_2(g) \rightarrow 2H_2O(g)$$

The reaction is exothermic because more energy is released making four new O–H bonds in the two water molecules than in breaking all the bonds in the oxygen and hydrogen molecules.

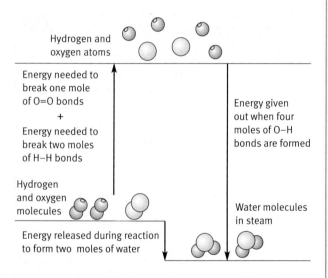

Hydrogen and oxygen atoms

Energy needed to break one mole of O=O bonds
+
Energy needed to break two moles of H–H bonds

Hydrogen and oxygen molecules

Energy released during reaction to form two moles of water

Energy given out when four moles of O–H bonds are formed

Water molecules in steam

**04.04 Energy level diagram for the combustion of hydrogen**

### TEST YOURSELF

2 **The energy needed to break a bond is the bond energy.**
H—H bond energy = 436 kJ mol$^{-1}$
I—I bond energy = 151 kJ mol$^{-1}$
H—I bond energy = 299 kJ mol$^{-1}$

**Calculate the overall energy change for the reaction**

$$H_2(g) + I_2(g) \rightarrow 2HI(g)$$

## Enthalpy changes in solution

Enthalpy changes for reactions in solution can be compared quickly using an expanded polystyrene cup with a lid as the calorimeter. Expanded polystyrene is an excellent insulator and has a negligible specific heat capacity.

If the reaction is exothermic the energy released cannot escape to the surroundings, so it heats up the solution.

If the reaction is endothermic no energy can enter from the surroundings, so the solution cools.

### WORKED EXAMPLE

On adding 0.48 g magnesium to 200 cm$^3$ of 1.0 mol dm$^{-3}$ hydrochloric acid the temperature rise is 10.5 °C. What is the enthalpy change for the reaction?

#### Notes on the method

Assume that the density of the solution is the same as water = 1 g cm$^{-3}$ and that for both the specific heat capacity, like water, is 4.2 J g$^{-1}$ K$^{-1}$.

#### Answer

The amount of magnesium
$$= 0.48 \text{ g} \div 24 \text{ g mol}^{-1} = 0.02 \text{ mol}$$

The amount of hydrochloric acid

$$= \frac{200}{1000} \text{ dm}^3 \times 1.0 \text{ mol dm}^{-3}$$

$$= 0.2 \text{ mol}$$

So the acid is in excess. The energy given out depends on the amount of magnesium.

Energy given out by the reaction and used to heat the water in the cup
$$= 200 \text{ g} \times 10.5 \text{ K} \times 4.2 \text{ J g}^{-1} \text{ K}^{-1} = 8820 \text{ J}$$

Energy given out per mole of magnesium
$$= 8820 \text{ J} \div 0.02 \text{ mol}$$
$$= 441\,000 \text{ J mol}^{-1}$$
$$= 441 \text{ kJ mol}^{-1}$$

The reaction is exothermic so the enthalpy change for the system is negative.

$$Mg(s) + 2HCl(aq) \rightarrow MgCl_2(aq) + H_2(g)$$
$$\Delta H = -441 \text{ kJ mol}^{-1}$$

Study and Revise AS and A2 Level Chemistry

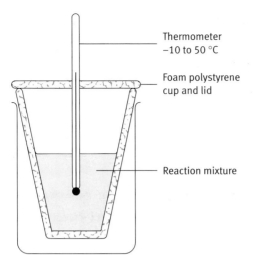

Thermometer
−10 to 50 °C

Foam polystyrene
cup and lid

Reaction mixture

**04.05 Measuring the enthalpy of a reaction in solution**

ℹ️ *The enthalpy change for a reaction, ΔH, is the energy change for the amounts (in moles) shown in the chemical equation.*

### Definition

The **standard enthalpy change of neutralisation** is the enthalpy change of reaction when an acid and an alkali neutralise each other under standard conditions (see Section 7.1).

### TEST YOURSELF

3  **On adding 25 cm³ of 1.0 mol dm⁻³ sulphuric acid to 25 cm³ 2.0 mol dm⁻³ sodium hydroxide in a plastic cup the temperature rise is 13 °C. Calculate the enthalpy change for the neutralisation reaction.**

## Standard enthalpy changes

Standard enthalpy changes are calculated under standard conditions. The standard temperature is 298 K (25 °C) and the standard pressure is 1 bar (= $10^5$ Pa = 100 kPa). The symbol for a standard enthalpy change is $\Delta H^{\ominus}_{298}$.

ℹ️ *The superscript sign in $\Delta H^{\ominus}_{298}$ shows that the value quoted is for standard conditions. The symbol is pronounced 'delta H standard'.*

It is important to specify the states of the chemicals. Equations should always include state symbols.

The standard states of elements and compounds are their most stable state under standard conditions. The standard state of carbon, for example, is graphite which is energetically more stable than diamond. The standard state of $H_2O$ is water (not ice or steam).

## Enthalpies of combustion

The standard enthalpy change of combustion of an element or compound is the enthalpy change when one mole of the substance burns completely in oxygen. The chemical and the products of burning must be in their normal stable (standard) states.

$$C_{graphite} + O_2(g) \rightarrow CO_2(g) \quad \Delta H^{\ominus}_{c,298} = -393.5 \text{ kJ mol}^{-1}$$

Like all thermochemical quantities the precise definition of standard enthalpy of combustion is important.

ℹ️ *For carbon and its compounds complete combustion means that all the carbon burns to carbon dioxide and that there is no soot or carbon monoxide.*

### Definition

The **standard enthalpy change of combustion** of a substance, $\Delta H^{\ominus}_{c,298}$, is the enthalpy change when one mole of the substance completely burns in oxygen under standard conditions with the reactants and products in their standard states.

ℹ️ *All combustion reactions are exothermic so $\Delta H_c$ values are always negative.*

### TEST YOURSELF

4  **The standard enthalpy of combustion of butane, $C_4H_{10}$, is −2876 kJ mol⁻¹. Write a balanced equation with state symbols for the reaction for which $\Delta H^{\ominus} = -2876$ kJ mol⁻¹.**

## Standard enthalpies of formation

The enthalpy change of formation of a compound is the enthalpy change when one mole of a compound is formed from its elements. The elements and the compound formed must be in their stable standard states.

For the standard enthalpy of formation of water:

$$H_2(g) + \tfrac{1}{2}O_2(g) \rightarrow H_2O(l) \quad \Delta H^{\ominus}_{f,298} = -286 \text{ kJ mol}^{-1}$$

> **i** *In thermochemistry the symbol $O_2$ represents one mole of oxygen molecules (that is 32 g oxygen) so $\frac{1}{2}O_2$ stands for half a mole of oxygen molecules (that is 16 g oxygen).*

Like all thermochemical quantities the precise definition of standard enthalpy of formation is important.

## Definition

The **standard enthalpy change of formation** of a compound, $\Delta H^{\ominus}_{f,298}$, is the enthalpy change when one mole of the compound forms from its elements under standard conditions with the elements and the compound in their standard states.

> **i** *The definition of standard enthalpy of formation means that by definition $\Delta H^{\ominus}_{f}$ [element] $= 0$ kJ mol$^{-1}$. There is no change and so no enthalpy change when an element forms from itself. In other words, the standard enthalpy of formation of an element is zero.*

## TEST YOURSELF

5  The standard enthalpy of formation of ethanol, $C_2H_5OH$, is $-277$ kJ mol$^{-1}$. Write a balanced equation with state symbols for the reaction for which $\Delta H^{\ominus} = -277$ kJ mol$^{-1}$.

6  By writing a balanced equation show that the standard enthalpy of formation of water is the same as the standard enthalpy change of combustion of hydrogen.

## Hess's law cycles

It is often not possible to measure standard enthalpy changes directly. Chemists have had to find an indirect method to measure them. They use Hess's law.

### Hess's law

Hess's law states that the energy change for a reaction is the same whether the reaction happens in one step or in a series of steps.

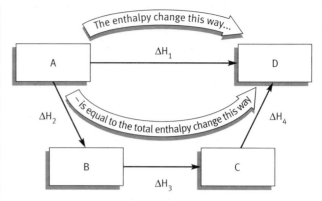

**04.06  A diagram to illustrate Hess's law.**
$\Delta H_1 = \Delta H_2 + \Delta H_3 + \Delta H_4$

> **i** *Hess's law is a chemical version of the law of conservation of energy.*

Hess's law makes it possible to calculate enthalpy changes that cannot be measured experimentally.

## Factfile

**Hess's Law**

Hess's law is used to calculate:

- standard enthalpies of formation from standard enthalpies of combustion

- standard enthalpies of reaction from standard enthalpies of formation.

## Enthalpies of formation from enthalpies of combustion

Figure 04.07 shows the energy cycle which chemists use to calculate enthalpies of formation from enthalpies of combustion.

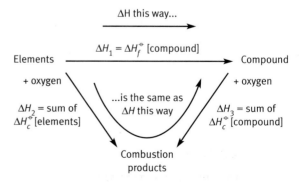

**04.07  A thermochemical cycle for calculating standard enthalpies of formation from standard enthalpies of combustion**

Study and Revise AS and A2 Level Chemistry

> ℹ️ *Reversing the direction of a reaction reverses the sign of ΔH but does not change its value.*

## WORKED EXAMPLE

Calculate the enthalpy of formation of butane, $C_4H_{10}$, at 298 K given these values for the standard enthalpies of combustion.

Standard enthalpies of combustion

$\Delta H_c^{\ominus}$[butane] $= -2876 \text{ kJ mol}^{-1}$

$\Delta H_c^{\ominus}$[carbon] $= -393 \text{ kJ mol}^{-1}$

$\Delta H_c^{\ominus}$[hydrogen] $= -286 \text{ kJ mol}^{-1}$

### Notes on the method

Draw the thermochemical cycle.

Pay careful attention to the signs. Put the value and sign for a quantity in brackets when multiplying, adding or subtracting enthalpy values.

### Answer

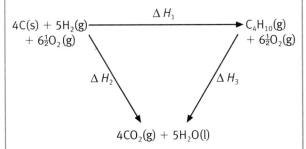

**04.08**

According to Hess's law $\Delta H_1 = \Delta H_2 - \Delta H_3$

$\Delta H_1 = \Delta H_f^{\ominus}[C_4H_{10}(g)]$

$\Delta H_2 = 4 \times \Delta H_c^{\ominus}[C_{graphite}] + 5 \times \Delta H_c^{\ominus}[H_2(g)]$

$\quad = 4 \times (-393 \text{ kJ mol}^{-1}) + 5 \times (-286 \text{ kJ mol}^{-1})$

$\quad = -3002 \text{ kJ mol}^{-1}$

$\Delta H_3 = \Delta H_c^{\ominus}[C_4H_{10}(g)] = -2876 \text{ kJ mol}^{-1}$

Hence:

$\Delta H_f^{\ominus}[C_4H_{10}(g)]$

$\quad = (-3002 \text{ kJ mol}^{-1}) - (-2876 \text{ kJ mol}^{-1})$

$\quad = -3002 \text{ kJ mol}^{-1} + 2876 \text{ kJ mol}^{-1}$

$\quad = -126 \text{ kJ mol}^{-1}$

### TEST YOURSELF

7  Use the values for standard enthalpies of combustion to calculate the standard enthalpies of formation of methane, $CH_4$.

Standard enthalpies of combustion:

$\Delta H_c^{\ominus}$[methane] $= -890 \text{ kJ mol}^{-1}$

$\Delta H_c^{\ominus}$[carbon] $= -393 \text{ kJ mol}^{-1}$

$\Delta H_c^{\ominus}$[hydrogen] $= -286 \text{ kJ mol}^{-1}$

## Standard enthalpies of reaction from standard enthalpies of formation

Thanks to Hess's law it is easy to calculate the enthalpy change for a reaction from values for standard enthalpies of formation.

### Definition

The **standard enthalpy change of a reaction** is the enthalpy change when the amounts shown in the chemical equation react. Like other standard quantities in thermochemistry, the standard enthalpy change for reaction is defined at 298 K, 1 bar pressure with the reactants and products in their normal stable states under these conditions. The concentration of any solutions is 1 mol dm$^{-3}$.

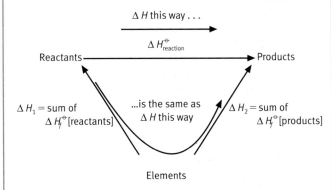

**04.09  Outline of a thermochemical cycle for calculating standard enthalpies of reaction from standard enthalpies of formation**

So Hess's law shows that: $\Delta H_{reaction} = -\Delta H_1 + \Delta H_2$

So $\Delta H_{reaction}^{\ominus} =$
{sum of $\Delta H_f^{\ominus}$ [products]} − {sum of $\Delta H_f^{\ominus}$ [reactants]}

Calculate the enthalpy change for the reaction of hydrazine with oxygen to form nitrogen and steam.

$\Delta H_f^{\ominus}[N_2H_4(l)] = +50.6 \text{ kJ mol}^{-1}$

$\Delta H_f^{\ominus}[H_2O(g)] = -241.8 \text{ kJ mol}^{-1}$

### Notes on the method

Write the balanced equation for the reaction.

Recall that by definition
$\Delta H_f^{\ominus}[\text{element}] = 0 \text{ kJ mol}^{-1}$

Pay careful attention to the signs. Put the value and sign for a quantity in brackets when multiplying, adding or subtracting enthalpy values.

### Answer

$N_2H_4(l) + O_2(g) \rightarrow N_2(g) + 2H_2O(g)$

$\Delta H_{\text{reaction}}^{\ominus} = \{\text{sum of } \Delta H_f^{\ominus}[\text{products}]\}$
$\qquad\qquad - \{\text{sum of } \Delta H_f^{\ominus}[\text{reactants}]\}$

$\Delta H_{\text{reaction}}^{\ominus} = \{\Delta H_f^{\ominus}[N_2(g)] + 2 \times \Delta H_f^{\ominus}[H_2O(g)]\}$
$\qquad\qquad - \{\Delta H_f^{\ominus}[N_2H_4(l)] + \Delta H_f^{\ominus}[O_2(g)]\}$

$\qquad = \{0 \text{ kJ mol}^{-1} + 2 \times (-241.8 \text{ kJ mol}^{-1})\}$
$\qquad\qquad - \{(+50.6 \text{ kJ mol}^{-1}) + (0 \text{ kJ mol}^{-1})\}$

$\qquad = (-483.6 \text{ kJ mol}^{-1}) - (50.6 \text{ kJ mol}^{-1})$

$\Delta H_{\text{reaction}}^{\ominus} = -534.2 \text{ kJ mol}^{-1}$

8 When calculating standard enthalpies of reactions involving water, why is it important to specify whether or not the $H_2O$ is present as water or as steam?

9 Calculate the standard enthalpy of reaction of ethene, $C_2H_4(g)$, with hydrogen to form ethane, $C_2H_6(g)$, given these values for standard enthalpies of formation:

$\Delta H_f^{\ominus}[C_2H_4(g)] = +52.2 \text{ kJ mol}^{-1}$

$\Delta H_f^{\ominus}[C_2H_6(g)] = -84.7 \text{ kJ mol}^{-1}$

## Enthalpy changes and covalent bonding

The enthalpy change for a reaction is the difference between the energy needed to break bonds in the reactants and the energy released as new bonds form in the products (see page 32).

The **bond dissociation enthalpy** is the enthalpy change on breaking one mole of a particular covalent bond in a gaseous molecule.

In molecules with two or more bonds between similar atoms, the energies needed to break successive bonds are not the same. In water, for example, the energy needed to break the first OH bond in $H-O-H(g)$ is 498 kJ mol$^{-1}$ but the energy needed to break the second $O-H$ bond in OH(g) is 428 kJ mol$^{-1}$.

*Dissociation is a change in which a molecule splits into two or more smaller particles.*

The mean values of bond enthalpies take into account the facts that:

- the successive bond dissociation enthalpies are not the same in compounds such as water or methane

- the bond dissociation enthalpy for a specific covalent bond varies slightly from one molecule to another.

**Average bond enthalpies** (or bond energies) are the average values of bond dissociation enthalpies used in approximate calculations to estimate enthalpy changes for reactions.

10 Use average bond enthalpies to estimate the enthalpy change when ethene, $H_2C=CH_2(g)$ reacts with gaseous hydrogen to form ethane, $CH_3-CH_3(g)$.

| Bond | Average bond enthalpy/kJ mol$^{-1}$ |
|------|------|
| C—C | 347 |
| C=C | 612 |
| H—H | 436 |
| C—H | 413 |

11 Which is likely to give a more accurate answer – calculating the enthalpy change for a reaction

- from average bond enthalpies?

- from enthalpies of formation?

## WORKED EXAMPLE

Use average bond enthalpies to estimate the enthalpy change for the reaction of methane with chlorine to form chloromethane and hydrogen chloride.

| Bond | Average bond enthalpy/kJ mol$^{-1}$ |
|------|------|
| C—H | 435 |
| C—Cl | 346 |
| Cl—Cl | 243 |
| H—Cl | 432 |

## Notes on the method

Write out the equation showing all the atoms and bonds in the molecules to make it easier to count the numbers of bonds broken and formed.

Ignore bonds that are unchanged. Just count the bonds broken and the new bonds formed.

## Answer

The equation for the reaction:

04.10

| Energy needed to break bonds/kJ mol$^{-1}$ | Energy given out as bonds form/kJ mol$^{-1}$ |
|------|------|
| $1 \times$ (C—H)  435 | $1 \times$ (C—Cl)  346 |
| $1 \times$ Cl—Cl  243 | $1 \times$ H—Cl  432 |
| Total = 678 | Total = 778 |

Less energy is needed to break bonds than is given out when bonds are formed so the reaction is exothermic and the enthalpy change is negative.

$\Delta H = +678$ kJ mol$^{-1} - 778$ kJ mol$^{-1} = -100$ kJ mol$^{-1}$

## Stability

In general, chemists expect that a reaction will go if it is exothermic.

Reactions that give out energy to their surroundings are the ones that happen spontaneously. This ties in with the common experience that change happens in the direction in which energy is spread around and dissipated in the surroundings.

So the sign of $\Delta H$ is a guide to the likely direction of change but it is not a totally reliable guide for two main reasons:

- First, the direction of change may depend on the conditions of temperature and pressure. One example is the condensation of a liquid. Steam condenses to water below 100 °C. This is an exothermic change. Above 100 °C the change goes in the opposite direction.

- Second, there are a few examples of endothermic reactions that go under normal conditions. So sometimes a reaction for which $\Delta H$ is positive can tend to happen. One example is the reaction of a solution of citric acid with sodium hydrogencarbonate. The mixture fizzes violently while cooling fast.

### Definition

A **spontaneous reaction** is one that tends to go. A reaction that naturally tends to go is still spontaneous even if it is very slow.

Even if a reaction tends to go, nothing may happen. The reaction may be highly exothermic and tend to go, yet the rate of change may be so slow that the mixture of chemicals is effectively inert. Turn on a Bunsen burner to mix methane gas and air – there is no change at room temperature. It takes a flame to start breaking bonds to get the exothermic reaction going (see Section 10.3).

## REVIEW

Copy and extend this Mind Map to cover all the ideas related to energy changes and chemical reactions. Include around your Mind Map the definitions of all the key terms.

Solving the 'test yourself' problems is an effective way of revising the ideas in this topic. Check your answers against the solutions on page 171. Where you feel the need for more practice, look for more examples in past examination papers and text books.

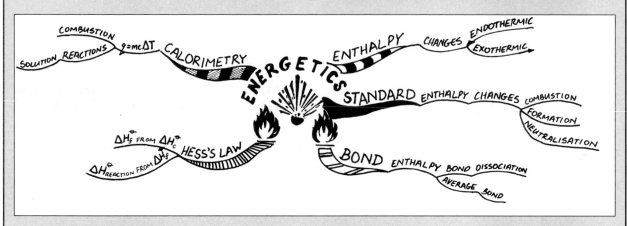

**04.11   Energetics Mind Map**

By the end of this topic you will be able to:

✔ remember that oxidation is a process of electron loss and reduction is a process of electron gain

✔ recognise some common oxidising agents and know that they vary in their oxidising strength

✔ recognise some common reducing agents and know that they vary in their reducing strength

✔ work out the oxidation states of elements in compounds, given the formulae of the compounds

✔ use oxidation numbers to recognise redox reactions

✔ write half-equations for the oxidation and reduction processes in redox reactions and combine the half equations to give an overall balanced equation.

## Electron transfer

### Redox

Redox reactions involve electron transfer. Reduction and oxidation always go together.

$$2Mg(s) \rightarrow 2Mg^{2+} + 4e^-$$

A metal is oxidised as it loses electrons forming positive ions.

$$O_2(g) + 4e^- \rightarrow 2O^{2-}$$

A non-metal is reduced as it gains electrons.

 *A memory aid (mnemonic)*

| *Oxidation* | *Reduction* |
|---|---|
| *Is* | *Is* |
| *Loss* | *Gain* |

**TEST YOURSELF**

1 Write equations to show the transfer of electrons in the reaction of:
   a magnesium with chlorine
   b copper with oxygen
   c lithium with iodine.

**Definition**

An **oxidising agent** can oxidise other atoms, molecules or ions by taking away electrons from them. Common oxidising agents are oxygen, chlorine, bromine and iodine, nitric acid, potassium manganate(VII), potassium dichromate(VI) and hydrogen peroxide.

All the halogens are oxidising agents. They differ in their oxidising strength: $Cl_2 > Br_2 > I_2$.

**Definition**

A **reducing agent** can reduce other atoms, molecules or ions by giving them electrons. Common reducing agents are hydrogen, zinc or iron in acid, and sulfur dioxide.

All the Group 2 metals are reducing agents. They differ in their reducing strength: $Ca > Mg > Be$

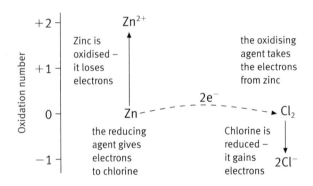

**05.01 Zinc is oxidised by loss of electrons. It is oxidised by the chlorine. So chlorine is the oxidising agent. At the same time chlorine gains electrons and is reduced by the zinc. The zinc is the reducing agent**

Bromine can oxidise iodide ions to iodine. This can be shown as two half equations:

- electron gain (reduction)
  $$Br_2(aq) + 2e^- \rightarrow 2Br^-(aq)$$

- electron loss (oxidation) $2I^-(aq) \rightarrow I_2(aq) + 2e^-$

The number of electrons gained must equal the number lost.

$$Br_2(aq) + 2e^- \rightarrow 2Br^-(aq)$$

$$2I^-(aq) \rightarrow I_2(aq) + 2e^-$$

$$Br_2(aq) + 2I^-(aq) \rightarrow 2Br^-(aq) + I_2(aq)$$

## TEST YOURSELF

2 **Write half equations for these redox reactions, then combine them to give the overall balanced equation.**

a **zinc displacing copper from copper(II) sulfate solution**

b **chlorine oxidising bromide ions to bromine**

c **chlorine oxidising aqueous iron(II) ions to iron(III) ions**

## Oxidation numbers

Chemists use oxidation numbers to:

- keep track of the numbers of electrons transferred or shared when the atoms of elements combine

- recognise redox reactions

- name inorganic compounds

- organise the chemistry of elements such as chlorine that can be oxidised or reduced to varying degrees (see Section 8.3).

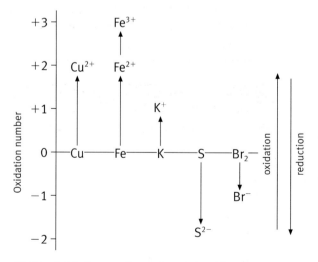

**05.02    Oxidation numbers of atoms and ions. Movement up the diagram involves the loss of electrons and a shift to more positive oxidation numbers – this is oxidation. Movement down the diagram involves gain of electrons and a shift to less positive or more negative oxidation numbers. This is reduction**

## Oxidation numbers and ions

Oxidation numbers show how many electrons are gained or lost by an element when atoms turn into ions.

With the help of the oxidation number rules it is possible to extend the use of oxidation numbers to ions consisting of more than one atom.

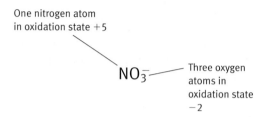

One nitrogen atom in oxidation state $+5$

$NO_3^-$

Three oxygen atoms in oxidation state $-2$

**05.03    The charge on an ion, such as the nitrate ion, is the sum of the oxidation numbers of the atoms. The normal oxidation state of oxygen is $-2$. There are three oxygen atoms (3 at $-2$) in the nitrate ion so the oxidation state of nitrogen must be $+5$ to give an overall charge on the ion of $1-$**

## Factfile

### Oxidation number rules

1 The oxidation numbers of uncombined elements are zero.

2 In simple ions the oxidation number of the element is the charge on the ion.

3 The sum of the oxidation numbers in a neutral compound is zero.

4 The sum of the oxidation numbers for an ion is the charge on the ion.

5 Some elements have fixed oxidation numbers in all their compounds.

| Metals | | Non-metals | |
|---|---|---|---|
| Group 1 metals (e.g. Li, Na, K) | $+1$ | hydrogen (except in metal hydrides, $H^-$) | $+1$ |
| Group 2 metals (e.g. Mg, Ca, Ba) | $+2$ | fluorine | $-1$ |
| aluminium | $+3$ | oxygen (except in peroxides, $O_2^{2-}$, and compounds with fluorine) | $-2$ |
| | | chlorine (except in compounds with oxygen and fluorine) | $-1$ |

> ℹ️ *Notice the use of 1– for the electric charge on a nitrate ion (number first for ionic charges) but the use of −2 to refer to the oxidation state of oxygen in the ion (charge first for oxidation states in ions and molecules).*

## Oxidation numbers and molecules

The oxidation number rules make it possible to extend the definition of oxidation and reduction to molecules.

> ℹ️ *In most molecules the oxidation state of an atom corresponds to the number of electrons from that atom which are shared in covalent bonds.*

Where two atoms are linked by covalent bonds the more electronegative atom (see page 24) has the negative oxidation state.

The reason for writing oxidation states as +1, +2 and so on is to make quite clear that when dealing with molecules they do not refer to electric charges. Molecules are not charged and the sum of the oxidation states for all the atoms in a molecule is zero.

$H_2SO_4$         $NH_3$         $F_2O$
+1 +6 −2       −3 +1       −1 +2

$ClO_3^-$         $NaH$         $AlCl_3$
+5 −2         +1 −1         +3 −1

**05.04   Oxidation states of elements in molecules and ions**

### TEST YOURSELF

3   What is the oxidation number of the following?
   a   iron in $Fe_2O_3$
   b   manganese in $MnO_4^-$
   c   carbon in $CaCO_3$
   d   nitrogen in the nitrite ion, $NO_2^-$
   e   nitrogen in hydrazine, $N_2H_4$.

4   Are these elements oxidised or reduced in these conversions?
   a   nickel to nickel sulfate
   b   bromine to silver bromide
   c   iodine to iodine chloride
   d   oxygen to water
   e   sodium to sodium hydride.

## Oxidation states and names of compounds

Oxidation numbers distinguish between the compounds of elements such as iron that can exist in more than one oxidation state. In iron(ɪɪ) chloride the Roman number ɪɪ shows that iron is in oxidation state +2. Iron atoms lose two electrons when they react with chlorine to make iron(ɪɪ) chloride.

### Factfile

**Rules for common inorganic names**

*   The ending −ide shows that a compound contains just two elements mentioned in the name. The more electronegative element comes second, for example, sodium sulfide, $Na_2S$, carbon dioxide, $CO_2$ and phosphorus trichloride, $PCl_3$.
*   The Roman numerals in names are the oxidation numbers of the elements, for example iron(ɪɪ) sulfate, $FeSO_4$ and iron(ɪɪɪ) sulfate, $Fe_2(SO_4)_3$.
*   The traditional names of oxoacids end −ic or −ous, as in sulfuric ($H_2SO_4$) and sulfurous ($H_2SO_3$) acids and nitric ($HNO_3$) and nitrous ($HNO_2$) acids, where the −ic ending is for the acid in which the central atom has the higher oxidation number.
*   The corresponding traditional endings for the salts of oxoacids are −ate and −ite as in nitrate, $NO_3^-$, and nitrite, $NO_2^-$.
*   The more systematic names for oxoacids and oxo salts use oxidation numbers as in sulfate(ᴠɪ) for sulfate, $SO_4^{2-}$, and sulfate(ɪᴠ) for sulfite, $SO_3^{2-}$.

### TEST YOURSELF

5   What are the names of these compounds?
   a   $MnO_2$
   b   $Cr_2O_3$
   c   $NaOCl$
   d   $KIO_3$
   e   $H_3PO_4$.

## Balancing redox equations

Oxidation numbers help to balance redox equations because the total decrease in oxidation number for the element reduced must equal the total increase in oxidation number for the element oxidised.

## WORKED EXAMPLE

What is the balanced equation for the reaction between $Fe^{2+}$ ions and an acidic solution of $MnO_4^-$ ions to form $Fe^{3+}$ ions, $Mn^{2+}$ ions and water molecules.

### Answer

Step 1 – Write down the formulae for the atoms, molecules and ions involved in the reaction.

In this example the hydrogen ions, $H^+$, in the acid take part in the reaction.

$$MnO_4^- + H^+ + Fe^{2+} \rightarrow Fe^{3+} + Mn^{2+} + H_2O$$

Step 2 – Identify the elements that change in oxidation number and the extent of change.

In this example only iron and manganese show changes of oxidation state.

$$MnO_4^- + H^+ + Fe^{2+} \rightarrow Mn^{2+} + H_2O + Fe^{3+}$$

change of +1

change of −5

Step 3 – Balance so that the total increase in oxidation number of one element equals the total decrease of the other element.

In this example the increase of +1 in the oxidation number of five iron(II) ions balances the −5 decrease of one manganate(VII) ion.

$$MnO_4^- + H^+ + 5Fe^{2+} \rightarrow Mn^{2+} + H_2O + 5Fe^{3+}$$

Step 4 – Balance for oxygen and hydrogen.

In this example the two oxygen atoms in the manganate(VII) ion react with eight hydrogen ions to form water molecules.

$$MnO_4^- + 8H^+ + 5Fe^{2+} \rightarrow Mn^{2+} + 4H_2O + 5Fe^{3+}$$

Step 5 – Add state symbols.

$$MnO_4^-(aq) + 8H^+(aq) + 5Fe^{2+}(aq)$$
$$\rightarrow Mn^{2+}(aq) + 4H_2O(l) + 5Fe^{3+}(aq)$$

## TEST YOURSELF

6 Write balanced equations for these redox reactions. State which element is oxidised and which is reduced in each example.
   a The reaction of ammonia gas, $NH_3$, with oxygen gas to form nitrogen monoxide gas, NO, and steam.
   b The reaction of aqueous thiosulfate ions, $S_2O_3^{2-}$, with iodine forming iodide ions and tetrathionate ions, $S_4O_6^{2-}$.
   c The reaction of aqueous iodide ions with an acidic solution of hydrogen peroxide, $H_2O_2$, forming iodine and water.
   d The reaction of copper metal with nitric acid to form copper(II) nitrate and nitrogen dioxide, $NO_2$.

## REVIEW

Solving the 'test yourself' problems is an effective way of revising the ideas in this topic. Check your answers against the solutions on page 171. Where you feel the need for more practice, look for more examples in past examination papers and text books.

**PREVIEW**

By the end of this topic you will be able to:

✔ remember that the elements in the periodic table are arranged in order of atomic number giving rise to periods and groups

✔ classify elements as s-, p- or d-block according to their position in the periodic table

✔ recall and explain in terms of structure and bonding the periodic patterns in the physical properties of the elements

✔ recall and explain in terms of electron configuration the periodic patterns in the properties of atoms of the elements

**TEST YOURSELF**

1 Write down the electron configurations of the atoms of these elements (showing the numbers of s, p and d electrons) and decide whether they are s-, p- or d-block elements: beryllium, nitrogen, potassium, titanium.

## Periodicity of physical properties of the elements

A repeating pattern is a periodic pattern. Hence the term 'periodicity'. Metals on the left conduct electricity; non-metals on the right are non-conductors. This reflects the underlying differences in structure and bonding.

The melting point of an element depends on both its structure and the type of bonding between the atoms.

The periodic trend for boiling points is similar to that for melting points.

## The periodic table

The elements in the periodic table are arranged in order of atomic number.

The horizontal rows in the periodic table are periods. The vertical columns are groups.

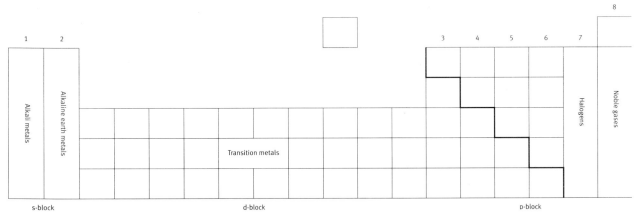

**06.01** **An outline periodic table showing the s-, p- and d-blocks. The stepped line separates metals on the left from non-metals on the right. the s-, p- and d-blocks are based on the electron configurations of the elements. So the modern arrangement of elements in the table reflects the underlying electron configurations of the atoms**

The s-block elements are the elements in Groups 1 and 2 on the left of the periodic table. For these elements the last electron added to the atomic structure goes into the s-orbital in the outer shell. All the elements in the s-block are reactive metals.

The p-block elements are the elements in Groups 3, 4, 5, 6, 7 and 8 in the periodic table. For these elements the last electron added to the atomic structure goes into one of the three p-orbitals in the outer shell.

The d-block elements are the elements in the three horizontal rows of elements in periods 4, 5 and 6 for which the last electron added to the atomic structure goes into a d-orbital.

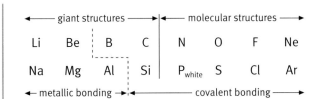

**06.02** **Structure and bonding in periods 2 and 3**

### Factfile

**Flame test colours**

| Metal ion | Colour |
|-----------|--------|
| magnesium | no colour |
| calcium | brick red |
| strontium | bright red |
| barium | pale green |

### TEST YOURSELF

**9** Write down the electron configuration of strontium.

**10** Explain why:

   **a** a magnesium ion is smaller than a magnesium atom

   **b** magnesium has a smaller atomic radius than calcium

   **c** magnesium has a larger first ionisation energy than calcium.

**11** Complete this spider diagram to summarise the reactions of magnesium giving the names and formulae of the products.

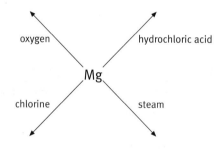

07.05

**12** Write equations for these reactions:

   **a** calcium with oxygen

   **b** magnesium with steam

   **c** strontium with chlorine

   **d** calcium oxide with water

   **e** barium carbonate with hydrochloric acid.

**13** Write an ionic equation for the reaction on mixing solutions of barium chloride and sodium sulfate.

## Thermal stability

Chemists explain differences in the properties of the compounds of these elements in terms of two factors:

• the charge on the metal ions, and

• the size of the metal ions.

---

Group 2 carbonates and nitrates are generally less stable than the corresponding Group 1 compounds. The larger the charge on the metal ion the less stable the compounds.

> ℹ️ *Whenever chemists use the term 'stability' they are making comparisons. For the Group 2 carbonates the question is: which is more stable, the metal carbonate or a mixture of the metal oxide and carbon dioxide?*

Down either Group 1 or Group 2 the carbonates become more stable. The larger the metal ion the more stable the compounds.

Chemists correlate the stability of compounds such as carbonates and nitrates with the polarising power of the metal ions. Generally, the greater the polarising power of the metal ion the less stable the carbonates and nitrates and the more easily they decompose to the oxide.

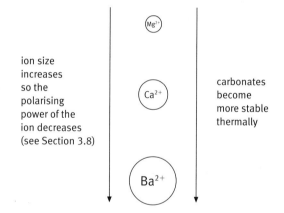

**07.06** Thermal stability of the Group 2 carbonates related to the polarising power of the metal ions

### TEST YOURSELF

**14** What does the term 'thermal stability' mean?

**15** Write equations for the decomposition of the carbonates of magnesium and calcium. Which carbonate decomposes at the lower temperature?

### REVIEW

**Add to your Mind Map of inorganic chemistry (see page 47) details about the chemistry of the s-block metals as required by the specification for your course.**

**By the end of this topic you will be able to:**

✔ **account for the physical properties of the halogen elements and the trends in these properties down the group**

✔ **describe reactions which show that all the halogens are oxidising agents but their reactivity decreases down the group**

✔ **recall that the hydrogen halides are gases which dissolve in water to form acid solutions**

✔ **know how the reactions with silver ions can be used to identify aqueous halide ions**

✔ **show that the reducing power of halide ions decreases down the group using the reactions with concentrated sulfuric acid as the example**

✔ **explain the formation of the +1 and +5 states of chlorine when the element reacts with water and with aqueous alkali**

✔ **explain the term 'disproportionation reaction'**

✔ **account for the use of chlorine for water treatment**

✔ **interpret the results of a redox titration to measure the strength of bleach**

✔ **give an account of the chemical changes involved in the extraction of bromine, and the manufacture of chlorine.**

## Halogen elements

The Group 7 elements are the halogens. They have similar chemical properties because they all have seven electrons in the outer shell – one less than the next noble gas in Group 8. The elements are all toxic.

fluorine, F    $1s^2 2s^2 2p^5$

chlorine, Cl    $1s^2 2s^2 2p^6 3s^2 3p^5$

bromine, Br    $1s^2 2s^2 2p^6 3s^2 3p^6 3d^{10} 4s^2 4p^5$

ℹ️ *The symbol X is often used to represent any halogen.*

The halogens consist of diatomic molecules, $X_2$, linked by a single covalent bond.

The halogens are all volatile – intermolecular forces increase down the group as the numbers of electrons in the atoms increase. Iodine atoms are the most polarisable (see Section 3.8). So melting points and boiling points rise down the group. Fluorine and chlorine are gases at room temperature, bromine is a liquid and iodine is a solid.

The halogen elements are highly electronegative. They form ionic compounds or compounds with polar bonding. Electronegativity decreases down the group.

The halogens are powerful oxidising agents. Fluorine is the strongest oxidising agent and iodine the weakest in the group.

Hot iron:

• burns brightly in chlorine forming iron(III) chloride

• glows as it reacts with bromine vapour forming iron(II) bromide

• reacts much less vigorously with iodine forming iron(II) iodide.

In Group 7, a more reactive halogen displaces a less reactive halogen. The order of reactivity for the halogens is Cl > Br > I. The more reactive halogen oxidises the ions of a less reactive halogen.

$$Br_2(aq) + 2I^-(aq) \rightarrow 2Br^-(aq) + I_2(s)$$

**Definition**

**Displacement reactions** are redox reactions that can be used to compare the relative strengths of non-metals as oxidising agents.

**TEST YOURSELF**

1 **Write down the full electron configuration of:**
   **a a fluoride ion**
   **b a chloride ion.**

2 **Write equations for the reactions between these elements and compounds:**
   **a iron with bromine**
   **b chlorine with bromide ions.**

3 **Write a half equation to show what happens to iodine molecules when they turn into iodide ions.**

4 **What colour changes occur on adding a solution of bromine to a solution of potassium iodide? How do you account for these changes?**

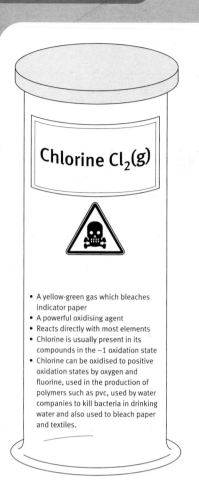

**Chlorine Cl₂(g)**

- A yellow-green gas which bleaches indicator paper
- A powerful oxidising agent
- Reacts directly with most elements
- Chlorine is usually present in its compounds in the −1 oxidation state
- Chlorine can be oxidised to positive oxidation states by oxygen and fluorine, used in the production of polymers such as pvc, used by water companies to kill bacteria in drinking water and also used to bleach paper and textiles.

**Bromine Br₂(l)**

- A dark-red liquid at room temperature
- Very volatile and gives off a choking orange vapour
- An oxidising element but a less powerful oxidising agent than chlorine
- Forms useful compounds such as bromomethane which kills soil pests and silver bromide which is used to make photographic film and paper.

**Iodine I₂(s)**

- A lustrous grey-black solid at room temperature
- Sublimes when gently warmed to give a purple vapour
- An oxidising agent but a less powerful oxidising agent than bromine
- Forms compounds which are useful as pharmaceuticals, photographic chemicals and dyes.

**08.01   Properties of chlorine, bromine and iodine**

## Halogen compounds

### Hydrogen halides

Hydrogen halides are compounds of hydrogen with the halogens. They are all colourless, molecular compounds with the formula HX where X stands for F, Cl, Br or I.

The bonds between hydrogen and the halogens are polar. The H—F bond is so polar that the properties of the compound are affected by hydrogen bonding (see pages 25–26).

Hydrogen chloride, hydrogen bromide and hydrogen iodide are similar in that they are:

- colourless gases at room temperature which fume in moist air

- very soluble in water forming acid solutions (hydrochloric, hydrobromic and hydriodic acids)

- strong acids so they ionise completely in water.

## Halide ions

Halide ions are the ions of the halogen elements. They include the fluoride, $F^-$, chloride, $Cl^-$, bromide, $Br^-$, and iodide, $I^-$, ions.

The reactions of halide ions with sulfuric acid show that there is a trend in the strength of the halide ions as reducing agents.

- Chloride ions do not reduce sulfuric acid at all, so the only gaseous product is hydrogen chloride gas.

- Bromide ions turn to orange bromine molecules as they reduce $H_2SO_4$ to $SO_2$, mixed with some hydrogen bromide gas.

- Iodide ions are the strongest reducing agents. They turn into iodine molecules as they reduce $H_2SO_4$ to S and $H_2S$; scarcely any hydrogen iodide forms.

So the trend as reducing agents is: $I^- > Br^- > Cl^-$.

**i** *In Group 7, iodine is the weakest oxidising agent so it has the least tendency to form negative ions. Conversely, iodide ions are the ones that most readily give up electrons and turn back into iodine molecules.*

## Testing for halide ions

Insoluble silver salts precipitate on mixing solutions of silver nitrate and a soluble chloride, bromide or iodide. Silver fluoride is soluble so there is no precipitate on adding silver nitrate to a solution of fluoride ions.

$$Ag^+(aq) + X^-(aq) \rightarrow AgX(s) \quad \text{where X = Cl, Br or I}$$

This precipitation reaction is used as a test for halide ions. The three silver compounds can be distinguished by their colour and the ease with which they redissolve in ammonia solution.

**i** *Acidify the unknown halide with nitric acid before testing with silver nitrate. This prevents the precipitation of other silver compounds.*

| Silver halide | Colour | Effect of adding ammonia solution to a precipitate of the compound |
|---|---|---|
| silver chloride, AgCl | white | redissolves readily in ammonia solution |
| silver bromide, AgBr | cream | redissolves but only in concentrated ammonia |
| silver iodide, AgI | yellow | does not redissolve in ammonia solution |

### TEST YOURSELF

5   Why is the boiling point of HF out of line with the trend for the other hydrogen halides (see page 26, Figure 03.29)?

6   Explain what is meant by the term 'strong acid' using hydrogen bromide as your example.

7   Write equations for the reactions of concentrated sulfuric acid with:
    a   sodium chloride
    b   potassium bromide.

8   Which of the reactions in question 7 is just an acid-base reaction and which involves a redox reaction?

## Oxoanions of chlorine

Chlorine oxoanions form when chlorine reacts with water and alkalis. In these compounds chlorine is oxidised to positive oxidation states through a series of disproportionation reactions.

### Definitions

An **oxoanion** is a negative ion of a non-metal combined with oxygen.

A **disproportionation reaction** is a reaction in which the same element both increases and decreases its oxidation number. It oxidises and reduces itself.

## Reactions with water

Chlorine dissolves in water. It reacts reversibly with water forming a mixture of weak chloric(I) acid and strong hydrochloric acid. This is an example of a disproportionation reaction.

$$Cl_2(aq) + H_2O(l) \rightleftharpoons HCl(aq) + HOCl(aq)$$

**i** *Memory aid (mnemonic) The 'hickle' (HCl) and 'hockle' (HOCl) reaction – to remember the products of the reaction of chlorine with water.*

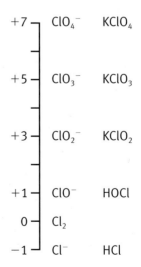

**08.02   Oxidation states of chlorine**

When chlorine dissolves in potassium (or sodium) hydroxide solution at room temperature it produces chlorate(I) and chloride ions.

$$Cl_2(aq) + 2OH^-(aq) \rightarrow ClO^-(aq) + Cl^-(aq) + H_2O(l)$$

On heating, the chlorate(I) ions disproportionate to chlorate(V) and chloride ions:

$$3ClO^-(aq) \rightarrow ClO_3^-(aq) + 2Cl^-(aq)$$

---

### TEST YOURSELF

9   Copy and complete this spider diagram to summarise the reactions of chlorine.

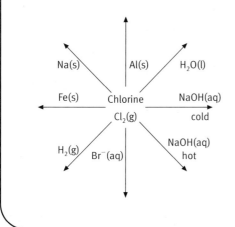

---

## Bleach

Chlorine and sodium chlorate(I) (bleach) are powerful disinfectants that quickly kill bacteria and other micro-organisms.

### Water treatment

Chlorine disinfects tap water by forming chloric(I) acid, HOCl. Choric(I) acid is a powerful oxidising agent and a weak acid. It is an effective disinfectant because the molecules can pass through the cell walls of bacteria and kill the organism by oxidising and chlorinating molecules that make up the structure of its cells.

### Bleach

Chlorine gas is very hazardous, so for household cleaning it is dissolved in sodium hydroxide to make domestic bleach, sodium chlorate(I). Sodium chlorate ionises fully in water.

$$NaOCl(aq) \rightarrow Na^+(aq) + OCl^-(aq)$$

Choric(I) acid is a weak acid so in bleach solution some of the chloric(I) ions take hydrogen ions from water molecules and turn into the un-ionised acid.

$$OCl^-(aq) + H^+(aq) \rightleftharpoons HOCl(aq)$$

---

## Analysing bleach

Chemists use an iodine-thiosulfate titration to measure the concentration of bleach. The method is based on the fact that oxidising agents such as bleach convert iodide ions to iodine quantitatively in acid conditions.

Adding acid reverses the reaction to form bleach and converts the chlorate and chloride ions to chlorine.

$$OCl^-(aq) + 2H^+(aq) \rightleftharpoons Cl_2(aq) + H_2O(aq)$$

The chlorine then oxidises iodide ions to iodine. So this technique measures the total 'available chlorine' in a solution of bleach.

$$Cl_2(aq) + 2e^- \rightarrow 2Cl^-(aq)$$

$$2I^-(aq) \rightarrow I_2(aq) + 2e^-$$

The iodine stays in solution in excess potassium iodide forming a yellow-brown colour.

The iodine produced is then titrated with a standard solution of sodium thiosulfate which reduces iodine molecules back to iodide ions. This also happens quantitatively, exactly as in the equation.

$$I_2(aq) + 2S_2O_3^{2-}(aq) \rightarrow 2I^-(aq) + S_4O_6^{2-}(aq)$$

The greater the amount of oxidising agent added, the more the iodine is formed and so the more thiosulfate is needed from a burette to react with it.

---

ℹ️ *On adding thiosulfate from a burette the colour of the iodine gets paler. Near the end-point the solution is a very pale yellow. Adding a little soluble starch solution as an indicator near the end-point gives a sharp colour change from blue-black to colourless. Starch solution gives an intense blue-black colour with iodine.*

---

### TEST YOURSELF

10  Some domestic bleach was diluted by measuring 5 cm³ of the bleach into a graduated flask and making the volume up to 50 cm³. Excess potassium iodide was added to 10.0 cm³ of the diluted bleach. The mixture was titrated with 0.090 mol dm⁻³ sodium thiosulfate solution. The titre was 22.4 cm³. Calculate the percentage of available chlorine in the undiluted bleach.

## WORKED EXAMPLE

A 5.0 cm³ sample of bleach was run into a flask from a burette and diluted with water. Excess potassium iodide was dissolved in the solution which was then acidified with dilute ethanoic acid. The iodine formed was titrated with a 0.05 mol dm⁻³ solution of sodium thiosulfate from a burette. The volume of sodium thiosulfate solution needed to decolourise the blue iodine-starch colour at the end-point was 24.5 cm³. Calculate the concentration of available chlorine in the bleach.

### Notes on the method

From the equations, work out the amount in moles of $S_2O_3^{2-}$ equivalent to 1 mol of available $Cl_2$.

There is then no need to consider the amounts of iodine in the calculations.

Look up the molar mass of chlorine:
$M_r(Cl_2) = 71.0$ g mol⁻¹.

Only use your calculator in the final stages of the calculation to avoid repeated rounding errors.

### Answer

From the equations, 1 mol $Cl_2$ produces 1 mol $I_2$ which then reacts with 2 mol $S_2O_3^{2-}$.

So 2 mol $S_2O_3^{2-}$ is equivalent to 1 mol $Cl_2$.

The amount of thiosulfate in 24.5 cm³
(= 0.0245 dm³) solution
$$= 0.0245 \text{ dm}^3 \times 0.05 \text{ mol dm}^{-3}$$

So the amount of $Cl_2$ in the flask
$$= 0.5 \times 0.0245 \text{ dm}^3 \times 0.05 \text{ mol dm}^{-3}$$

The available chlorine came from 5.0 cm³
$$= 0.005 \text{ dm}^3 \text{ of the diluted bleach.}$$

So the concentration of the bleach
$$= (0.5 \times 0.0245 \text{ dm}^3 \times 0.05 \text{ mol dm}^{-3}) \div 0.005 \text{ dm}^3$$
$$= 0.123 \text{ mol dm}^{-3}$$

The mass concentration
$$= 0.123 \text{ mol dm}^{-3} \times 71.0 \text{ g mol}^{-1} = 8.73 \text{ g dm}^{-3}$$

## Manufacture of halogens

### The chlor-alkali industry

Electrolysis of sodium chloride solution (brine) is the basis of the chlor-alkali industry. Electrolysis of brine is used to manufacture chlorine, hydrogen and sodium hydroxide.

During electrolysis, chlorine forms at the positive electrode (anode). Hydrogen bubbles off the negative electrode (cathode) while the solution turns into sodium hydroxide.

The cell used for electrolysis of brine has to be carefully designed because chorine reacts with sodium hydroxide. The cell has to keep the chlorine and sodium hydroxide apart.

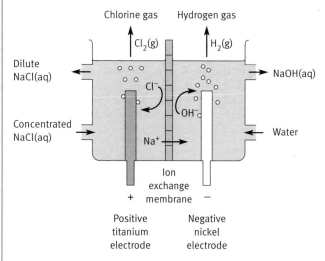

**08.03** **Main inputs and outputs of a membrane cell. The membrane allows the solution to pass through but stops the chlorine mixing with the alkali. The membrane has ion exchange properties. It lets positive ions through but not negative ions**

### Bromine extraction

Industry extracts bromine from sea water (see Figure 08.04) or natural brine. A four stage process concentrates and separates the bromine from sea water which contains about 65 parts per million bromide ions.

### TEST YOURSELF

11 a Write equations for the electrode processes during the electrolysis of brine. Which element is oxidised during the process and which element is reduced?
   b How does sodium hydroxide solution form in this process?
   c Why is it important to keep the chlorine and the sodium hydroxide apart during the electrolysis of brine?
   d What can be made by allowing the chlorine and the sodium hydroxide to mix?

12 Write equations for the reactions involved in the extraction of bromine. Use oxidation numbers to decide which chemicals are oxidised and which are reduced in these reactions.

**1 Oxidation of bromide ions to bromine**
Sea water is filtered and acidified to pH 3.5 to prevent chlorine and bromine reacting with water. Then chlorine displaces bromine.

**2 Separation of bromine vapour**
A blast of air through the reaction mixture carries away the displaced bromine and helps to concentrate it.

**3 Formation of hydrobromic acid**
The air with bromine vapour meets sulfur dioxide gas and a fine mist of water producing hydrobromic acid, which is ionised in solution. The sulfur dioxide turns into sulfate ions. After this stage the concentration of bromine in the solution is 1500 times greater than in sea water.

**4 Displacement and purification of bromine**
The solution from stage 3 now flows down a tower, while a mixture of chlorine gas and steam passes up it. The chlorine oxidises bromide ions to bromine which evaporates in the steam. The mixture of steam and bromine is cooled and condensed producing a dense lower bromine layer under a layer of water

**08.04** **Extraction of bromine from sea water. Natural brines contain more bromine than sea water so that only stage 4 is needed to separate the bromine**

## REVIEW

**Add to your Mind Map of inorganic chemistry (see page 47) details relevant to the specification for your course about:**

- **the chemistry of Group 7 (the halogens)**
- **industrial processes involving the halogens.**

## Extraction of iron from its oxide using carbon

### Making iron

Industry produces iron from its oxide ores in large blast furnaces.

Coke burning in air heats the furnace.

$$C(s) + O_2(g) \rightarrow CO_2(g)$$

Coke also produces the reducing agent by reacting with carbon dioxide further up the furnace to make carbon monoxide.

$$C(s) + CO_2(g) \rightarrow 2CO(g)$$

The carbon monoxide reduces the ore to iron.

$$Fe_2O_3(s) + 3CO(g) \rightarrow 2Fe(l) + 3CO_2(g)$$

Where the furnace is hot enough, carbon too can act as the reducing agent.

Limestone, $CaCO_3$, decomposes to calcium oxide, $CaO$, which combines with silicon dioxide and other impurities to make a liquid slag. For example:

$$CaO(s) + SiO_2(s) \rightarrow CaSiO_3(l)$$

The molten metal and slag run to the bottom of the furnace. The slag floats on the metal so it can be tapped off separately.

### Making steel

Steels are alloys of iron with carbon and with other metals.

Steel is made by the basic oxygen steelmaking (BOS) process which removes impurities from iron extraction in a blast furnace.

Stage 2 converts impurities in the liquid metal, such as carbon, silicon and phosphorus, into their oxides.

- Carbon dioxide escapes as a gas.
- The acidic oxides of the non-metals, silicon and phosphorus, react with calcium oxide to form a molten slag. The slag floats on the surface of the liquid steel and can be poured off separately.

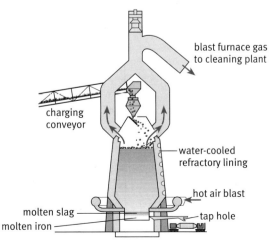

**09.01 Diagram of a blast furnace for extracting iron**

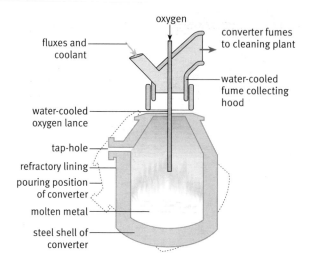

oxygen

converter fumes
to cleaning plant

fluxes and
coolant

water-cooled
fume collecting
hood

water-cooled
oxygen lance

tap-hole

refractory lining

pouring position
of converter

molten metal

steel shell of
converter

**09.02  Basic oxygen converter for making steel**

---

**Definition**

An **acidic oxide** is an oxide of a non-metal that reacts with water to form an acid. Some acidic oxides are insoluble but they can be recognised because they react directly with basic oxides to form salts.

---

**TEST YOURSELF**

1  Write equations for these reactions in a blast furnace:
   a  the reduction of iron ore by carbon
   b  the decomposition of limestone to calcium oxide.

2  Write equations for the reactions used to remove these impurities during steel making:
   a  sulfur
   b  silicon (2 reactions)
   c  excess oxygen.

---

## Extraction of aluminium by electrolysis

The main ore of aluminium is bauxite, which consists of impure aluminium oxide. Impurities are removed by heating powdered bauxite with sodium hydroxide solution. Aluminium oxide, which is amphoteric (see page 127), dissolves but other oxides, such as iron(III) oxide and titanium(IV) oxide, do not. After filtering, seed crystals are added and hydrated aluminium oxide crystallises as the solution cools. Heating the hydrated crystals at 1000 °C produces anhydrous aluminium oxide, $Al_2O_3$, ready for aluminium extraction.

---

Aluminium is obtained by electrolysis of a solution of aluminium oxide in molten sodium aluminium fluoride, $Na_3AlF_6$. Pure aluminium oxide for the process is obtained by purifying bauxite.

---

**i** $Na_3AlF_6$ *is essential to the process because the pure oxide melts at 2015 °C – much too high for an industrial process.*

---

Reduction at the cathode: $Al^{3+} + 3e^- \rightarrow Al$

The aluminium is liquid at the temperature of the molten electrolyte (970 °C) and it collects at the bottom of the pot. The molten metal is tapped off from time to time.

Oxidation at the anode: $2O^{2-} \rightarrow O_2 + 4e^-$

Much of the oxygen reacts with the carbon of the anodes forming carbon dioxide. The anodes burn away and have to be replaced regularly.

The waste gases from the cell contain fluorides and have to be thoroughly cleaned to avoid pollution of the region surrounding the plant.

---

**TEST YOURSELF**

3  Explain the use of sodium hydroxide to purify aluminium oxide.

4  Why are plants for extracting aluminium often built near to hydroelectric power stations?

5  Why do the graphite anodes have to be replaced regularly?

6  What are the benefits of aluminium that make it worth extracting the metal by an expensive process?

---

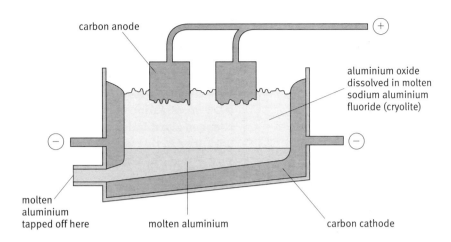

**09.03  Cross sectional diagram of an electrolysis cell for extracting aluminium**

## Extraction of titanium by reduction of its chloride

The ores of titanium are rutile, $TiO_2$ and ilmenite, $FeTiO_3$. Titanium is the fourth most abundant metal in the Earth's crust and it would be more widely used if the methods of extraction were less difficult and expensive. In theory it should be possible to extract titanium from its oxide with carbon, but in practice some of the titanium reacts with carbon forming carbides, which make the metal brittle.

After purifying the ore, it is heated with carbon in a stream of chlorine gas at about 800 °C.

$$TiO_2 + 2Cl_2 + C \rightarrow TiCl_4 + CO_2$$

The titanium(IV) chloride condenses as a liquid that can be purified by fractional distillation.

The chloride can be reduced to the metal using sodium or magnesium. The UK method uses sodium. Titanium chloride passes into a reactor containing molten sodium at 500 °C in an inert argon atmosphere. Exactly the right amount of the chloride is added to react with all the sodium. The reaction is exothermic and so the temperature rises.

$$TiCl_4 + 4Na \rightarrow Ti + 4NaCl$$

The reactor is kept hot for about two days, then it is removed from the furnace and allowed to cool. The solid product is crushed and the sodium chloride dissolved away with dilute hydrochloric acid leaving the titanium metal, which is then washed and dried.

> **i** *Titanium is mainly used to make aircraft engines and airframes. Other major uses are the production components of chemical plants, such as heat exchangers.*

## Recycling

### Recycling steel

Recycling steel can be done repeatedly because it is as good as new after reprocessing. Recycling saves energy and also cuts down on the amount of water needed to make iron since large quantities of water are involved in mineral processing.

Worldwide, the steel industry recycles over 430 million tonnes of the metal each year, which is a recycling rate of over 50%. The basic oxygen process uses a minimum of 25% scrap steel. Electric arc furnaces make steel plate, beams and bars by remelting nearly 100% scrap steel. Much of the recycled steel is waste from various stages of manufacturing steel objects. Another large source of scrap is from old motor vehicles.

### Recycling aluminium

Aluminium scrap from manufacturing processes is always recycled. Less than one percent of the mass of household waste is aluminium; almost all of it in the form of drinks cans. Aluminium is not magnetic but can be separated from a waste stream by a rapidly varying magnetic field which induces eddy currents in the metal of the can. The magnetic effect of the eddy currents leads to a force which pushes the cans out of the waste.

Recycling reduces environmental harm by cutting the use of raw materials and hence the scale of mining and mineral processing. Recycling is also cost effective because the energy needed to manufacture aluminium from bauxite is so high. Using recycled cans instead of bauxite, for example, allows the industry to make 20 times as many cans for the same amount of energy.

## TEST YOURSELF

9 Why are metals easier to recycle than plastics?

10 Make a list of the benefits of recycling metals.

## REVIEW

Metals extraction involves reducing metals from positive oxidation states in their compounds to the zero oxidation state of the free element. Draw an oxidation number diagram to chart the changes of oxidation number in the processes described in this section.

Add to your Mind Map of inorganic chemistry (see page 47) details about the extraction of metals. Check which methods you are required to recall from the specification for your course.

**PREVIEW**

**By the end of this topic you will be able to:**

✔ recall the factors which affect rates of reaction and explain their effects in terms of collision theory

✔ understand the term 'activation energy'

✔ use plots showing the Maxwell-Boltzman distribution at different temperatures to account for the effects of temperature and catalysts on reaction rates

✔ give examples of homogeneous and heterogeneous catalysts

✔ distinguish between kinetic and thermodynamic stability.

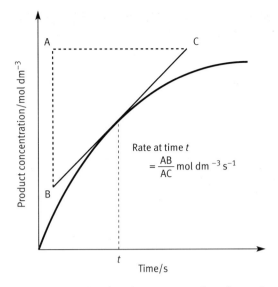

Rate at time $t$
$$= \frac{AB}{AC} \text{ mol dm}^{-3}\,\text{s}^{-1}$$

**10.01  A graph showing the concentration of a product plotted against time. The gradient at any point measures the rate of reaction**

## Factors affecting rates of reaction

### Measuring reaction rates

The amounts or concentrations of chemicals change during any chemical reaction. Products form as reactants disappear. The rates at which these changes happen give a measure of the rate of reaction.

> ℹ️ *Chemical equations say nothing about how quickly the changes occur. Chemists have to do experiments to measure the rates of reaction under various conditions.*

Chemists design their rate experiments to measure a property which changes with the amount or concentration of a reactant or product.

$$\text{rate of reaction} = \frac{\text{change recorded in the property}}{\text{time for the change}}$$

In most chemical reactions the rate changes with time. The graph in Figure 10.01 is steepest at the start when the reaction is at its fastest. As the reaction continues it slows down until it finally stops. This happens because one of the reactants is being used up.

### Concentration

In general, the higher the concentration of the reactants, the faster the reaction.

For gas reactions a change in pressure has the same effect as changing the concentration. A higher pressure compresses a mixture of gases and increases their concentration.

### Surface area of solids

Breaking a solid into smaller pieces increases the surface area in contact with a liquid or gas. This speeds up any reaction happening at the surface of the solid.

> **Definition**
>
> A **heterogeneous reaction** involves chemicals in more than one phase, for example the reaction between a solid and a solution or between a solid and a gas.

### Temperature

Raising the temperature is a very effective way of increasing the rate of a reaction. Typically a 10° rise in temperature roughly doubles the rate of reaction.

### Catalysts

Catalysts speed up the rates of chemical reactions without themselves changing permanently. Catalysts can be recovered at the end of the reaction. Often a small amount of catalyst is effective.

Many catalysts are specific to a particular reaction. This is especially true of enzymes.

Catalysts speed up reactions but they do not change the position of equilibrium for a reversible reaction (see Section 11.3).

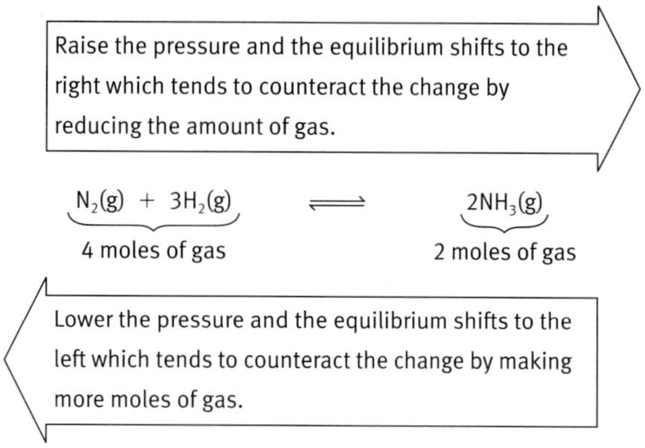

Raise the pressure and the equilibrium shifts to the right which tends to counteract the change by reducing the amount of gas.

$$N_2(g) + 3H_2(g) \rightleftharpoons 2NH_3(g)$$

4 moles of gas       2 moles of gas

Lower the pressure and the equilibrium shifts to the left which tends to counteract the change by making more moles of gas.

**11.04**

## Changing the temperature

If the temperature rises, the equilibrium shifts in the direction that is endothermic. If the temperature falls, the equilibrium shifts in the direction that is exothermic.

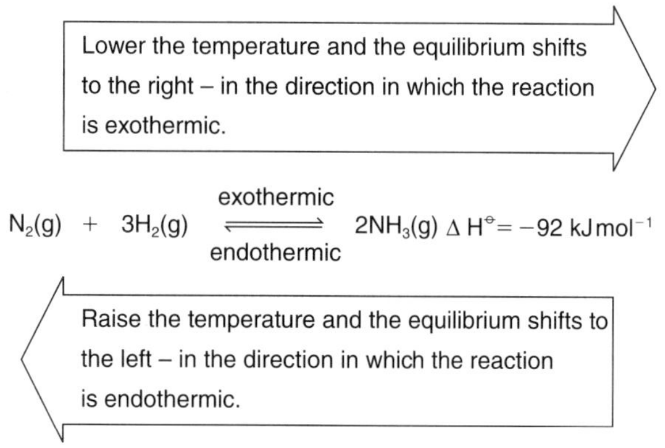

Lower the temperature and the equilibrium shifts to the right – in the direction in which the reaction is exothermic.

$$N_2(g) + 3H_2(g) \underset{\text{endothermic}}{\overset{\text{exothermic}}{\rightleftharpoons}} 2NH_3(g) \quad \Delta H^\circ = -92 \text{ kJ mol}^{-1}$$

Raise the temperature and the equilibrium shifts to the left – in the direction in which the reaction is endothermic.

**11.05**

## Chemical equilibrium in industry

### Manufacturing sulfuric acid

The Contact Process produces sulfuric acid from sulfur, The process produces over 150 million tonnes of the acid in the world each year.

Absorbtion
$$H_2O(l) + SO_3(g) \longrightarrow H_2SO_4(l)$$
Sulfur dioxide cannot be dissolved in water directly because the violent reaction produces a hazardous mist of acid. Instead the gas is absorbed in 98% sulfuric acid. Sulfur trioxide passes up a tower packed with pieces of ceramic down which the concentrated acid trickles. The circulating acid is kept at the same strength by drawing off product while adding water.

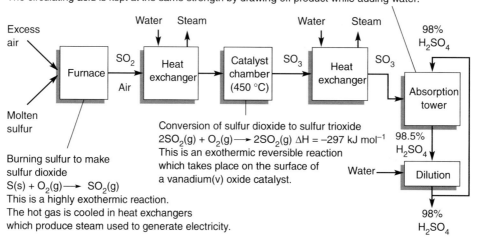

Excess air

Molten sulfur

Burning sulfur to make sulfur dioxide
$$S(s) + O_2(g) \longrightarrow SO_2(g)$$
This is a highly exothermic reaction.
The hot gas is cooled in heat exchangers which produce steam used to generate electricity.

Conversion of sulfur dioxide to sulfur trioxide
$$2SO_2(g) + O_2(g) \longrightarrow 2SO_2(g) \quad \Delta H = -297 \text{ kJ mol}^{-1}$$
This is an exothermic reversible reaction which takes place on the surface of a vanadium(V) oxide catalyst.

**11.06 Outline flow diagram for the manufacture of sulfuric acid**

Raising the temperature of an equilibrium mixture of $SO_2$, $O_2$ and $SO_3$ lowers the percentage conversion to $SO_3$ but the temperature must be high enough to make the reaction go fast enough. The catalyst is not active below 380 °C and works best at about 550 °C.

Increasing the pressure would increase the conversion to sulfur dioxide but the extra cost is not usually justified.

Typically, the gas mixture passes through four catalyst beds. Between each bed the gas mixture is cooled in a heat exchanger and cold air with more oxygen is added to the mixture. After the third bed the level of conversion is 98%. To ensure conversion of the remaining $SO_2$, sulfur trioxide is absorbed from the gas stream and more air is added before the gases flow through the fourth bed of catalyst.

Environmental legislation requires very low emissions of acid gases into the air. A modern plant converts 99.7% of the sulfur dioxide into sulfuric acid in stages 2 and 3.

> **i** *Sulfuric acid is needed on a large scale to make many other chemicals, including phosphate fertilisers, paints and pigments, detergents, plastics, fibres and dyes.*

## Manufacturing ammonia

The Haber process makes ammonia by combining nitrogen with hydrogen in the presence of an iron catalyst.

Hydrogen for the process comes from natural gas and steam. The nitrogen comes from the air.

The reaction is very slow at room temperature. An iron catalyst makes it possible for the reaction to go fast

enough without the temperature being so high that the yield is too low.

The process typically operates at pressures between 70 atmospheres and 200 atmospheres with temperatures in the range 400 °C to 600 °C.

Le Chatelier's principle helps to explain the conditions chosen for ammonia manufacture by the Haber process.

> **i** *The main uses of ammonia are: making fertilisers (80%), making nylon (7%) and nitric acid manufacture (5%).*

## Manufacturing nitric acid

A two-stage process converts ammonia to nitric acid.

### Factfile

#### Manufacture of nitric acid

*Stage 1*: Oxidation of ammonia by oxygen air on the surface of a catalyst gauze made of an alloy of platinum and rhodium.

$$4NH_3(g) + 5O_2(g) \rightleftharpoons 4NO(g) + 6H_2O(g)$$
$$\Delta H = -909 \text{ kJ mol}^{-1}$$

The exothermic reaction keeps the catalyst glowing red hot at about 900 °C. The pressure is typically about 10 times atmospheric pressure.

*Stage 2*: Absorption of nitrogen oxides in water in the presence of oxygen to make nitric acid.

$$2NO(g) + O_2(g) \rightleftharpoons 2NO_2(g)$$
$$4NO_2(g) + O_2(g) + 2H_2O(l) \rightarrow 4HNO_3(aq)$$

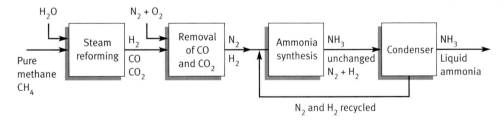

**11.07  Flow diagram for the synthesis of ammonia**

**PREVIEW**

By the end of this topic you will be able to:

✔ recognise and name primary, secondary and tertiary halogenoalkanes

✔ recall the reagents and conditions for the reactions of halogenoalkanes with potassium hydroxide, potassium cyanide and ammonia

✔ recall that the hydrolysis of nitriles produces carboxylic acids

✔ correlate the relative reactivity of halogenoalkanes with factors such as bond strength and bond polarity

✔ describe the bond breaking and bond forming during nucleophilic substitution reactions and during the elimination of a hydrogen halide

✔ explain how to test for the halide group in a halogenoalkane

✔ recall some of the uses of halogenoalkanes.

## Structures and names of halogenoalkanes

Halogenoalkanes are compounds formed by replacing one or more of the hydrogen atoms in alkanes with halogen atoms.

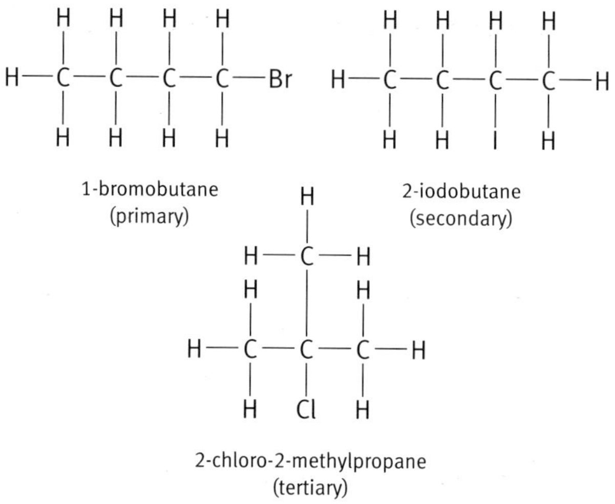

H H H H
| | | |
H—C—C—C—C—Br
| | | |
H H H H
1-bromobutane
(primary)

H H H H
| | | |
H—C—C—C—C—H
| | | |
H H I H
2-iodobutane
(secondary)

H
|
H—C—H
|
H   H
|   |
H—C—C—C—H
|   |   |
H   Cl  H
2-chloro-2-methylpropane
(tertiary)

**14.01   Names and structures of some halogenoalkanes**

 *A primary halogenoalkane has the halogen atom at the end of the chain.*

 *A secondary compound has the halogen atom somewhere along the chain but not at the ends.*

 *A tertiary halogenoalkane has the halogen atom at a branch in the chain.*

**TEST YOURSELF**

1 Draw the structures of these compounds and identify the primary, secondary and tertiary compound.
 a 1- chloropentane
 b 2-bromo-2-methylpropane
 c 2-iodobutane.

## Properties of halogenoalkanes
### Physical properties

Chloromethane, bromomethane and chloroethane are gases at room temperature. Most other halogenoalkanes are colourless liquids that do not mix with water.

### Chemical reactions

The characteristic reactions of halogenoalkanes are nucleophilic substitution reactions.

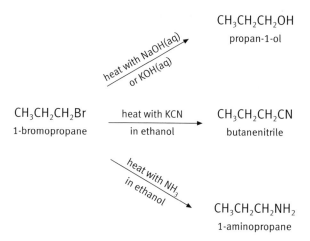

CH₃CH₂CH₂OH
propan-1-ol

heat with NaOH(aq) or KOH(aq)

CH₃CH₂CH₂Br
1-bromopropane

heat with KCN in ethanol → CH₃CH₂CH₂CN
butanenitrile

heat with NH₃ in ethanol → CH₃CH₂CH₂NH₂
1-aminopropane

**14.02   Substitution reactions of 1-bromopropane**

The rates of reaction of halogenoalkanes are in the order: RI > RBr > RCl where R represents an alkyl group.

The C—I bond is the longest and the weakest (as measured by the mean bond enthalpy). The C—Cl bond is the shortest and the strongest. Bond polarity does not appear to be a factor in determining the rates because chlorine is the most electronegative of the elements, so the C—Cl bond is the most polar.

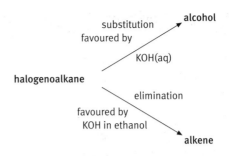

### 14.04 The alternative reactions with a solution of hydroxide ions

## Factfile

### Adding a carbon atom to the chain

Nitriles are useful intermediates in organic synthesis, especially when there is a need to add to the carbon skeleton of the molecule.

Hydrolysis converts a nitrile to a carboxylic acid. Acids or alkalis can catalyse this reaction.

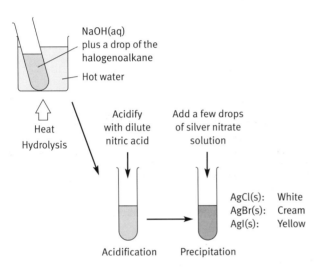

NaOH(aq) plus a drop of the halogenoalkane

Hot water

Heat
Hydrolysis

Acidify with dilute nitric acid

Add a few drops of silver nitrate solution

AgCl(s): White
AgBr(s): Cream
AgI(s): Yellow

Acidification    Precipitation

**14.03** The hydrolysis of halogenoalkanes makes it possible to distinguish chloro-, bromo- and iodo- compounds. Heating the compound with alkali releases halide ions. Acidifying with nitric acid and then adding silver nitrate produces a precipitate of the silver halide

> ℹ️ *Hydrolysis is a reaction in which a compound is split apart in a reaction involving water. Hydrolysis reactions are often catalysed by acids or alkalis.*

## Definition

An **elimination reaction** is a reaction that splits off a simple compound from a molecule to form a double bond.

Elimination of a hydrogen halide from a halogenoalkane produces an alkene. The elimination is favoured if the halogen atom is in the middle of the carbon chain or at a branch in the chain. The conditions are to heat the halogenoalkane with a solution of potassium hydroxide in ethanol.

### 14.05 Elimination of hydrogen bromide from 2-bromobutane

> ℹ️ *Hydrolysis leading to substitution is much more likely using potassium or sodium hydroxide dissolved in water.*

> ℹ️ *Elimination is more likely if there is no water and the alkali is dissolved in ethanol.*

## TEST YOURSELF

2  Which of these molecules are polar and which are non-polar: $CHCl_3$, $CH_2Br_2$, $CHI_3$ and $CCl_4$?

3  Compare the boiling points of the isomers 1-chlorobutane, 2-chlorobutane and 2-chloro-2-methylpropane. Suggest an explanation for the differences in boiling points of the primary, secondary and tertiary compounds.

4  Write equations for these reactions and give the conditions for the reaction.
   a  1-bromoethane with aqueous sodium hydroxide
   b  1-bromoethane with potassium cyanide followed by hydrolysis with dilute hydrochloric acid
   c  1-chloropropane with a solution of ammonia in ethanol
   d  2-bromo-2-methylpropane with a solution of potassium hydroxide in ethanol.

## Reaction mechanisms

### Nucleophilic substitution

Halogen atoms are more electronegative than carbon atoms, so a carbon-halogen bond is polar. This makes the carbon atom open to attack by reagents attracted to positive charges.

> ### Definition
>
> **Nucleophiles** are molecules or ions with a lone-pair of electrons that can form a new covalent bond. Nucleophiles are reagents that attack molecules where there is a partial positive charge, $\delta+$. They seek out positive charges – they are 'nucleus-loving'.

Nucleophilic attack on the carbon atom of the C—X bond in a halogenoalkane, RX, leads to a substitution reaction, where X = Cl, Br or I.

The suggested mechanism shows the C—Br bond breaking as the nucleophile, $OH^-$, forms a new bond with carbon.

**14.06   The nucleophile is the $OH^-$ ion**

### Elimination reactions

The same reagents that can act as nucleophiles can also form dative bonds with hydrogen ions, $H^+$, so they can also act as bases. This is particularly true of the hydroxide ion. Heating a halogenoalkane with a base can bring about elimination of a hydrogen halide instead of substitution.

**14.07   Mechanism for the elimination of hydrogen bromide from 2-bromopropane**

> ### Definition
>
> An **elimination reaction** splits off a simple compound from a molecule to form a double bond.

> ### TEST YOURSELF
>
> 5   Give three examples of nucleophiles that can attack a halogenoalkane leading to substitution. What do the three examples have in common?
>
> 6   Show that the hydroxide ion acts as a base when it causes the elimination of a hydrogen halide from a halogenoalkane.

## Uses of halogenoalkanes

Halogenoalkanes are important to organic chemists both in laboratories and in industry. The reason is that they are reactive compounds that can be converted in other more valuable products. This makes them useful as intermediates when converting one chemical to another.

Some halogenoalkanes are valuable for their own sake. They are also used as:

- solvents (for example dichloromethane)
- refrigerants (for example hydrochlorofluorocarbons, such as $CHClF_2$, which are replacing CFCs)
- pesticides (for example bromomethane)
- fire extinguishers (for example $CBr_2ClF$).

> **i** *There are growing restrictions on the uses of many halogenoalkanes because of concern about their hazards to health, their persistence in the environment and their effect on the ozone layer.*

> ### REVIEW
>
> Add to your collection of revision cards to learn the organic reactions of halogenoalkanes (see page 81).
>
> Extend your Mind Map of organic chemistry (see page 76) by adding more about:
>
> - the reactions of halogenoalkanes
> - nucleophilic substitution and elimination reactions.

## Structures and names of alcohols

Alcohols are compounds with the formula R—OH where R represents an alkyl group. The hydroxy group —OH gives the compounds their characteristic reactions.

IUPAC rules name alcohols by changing the ending of the corresponding alkane to –ol. So ethane becomes ethanol.

## Properties of alcohols

### Physical properties

Even the simplest alcohols, such as methanol and ethanol, are liquids at room temperature because of hydrogen bonding between the —OH groups. Alcohols

$CH_3$—$CH_2$—$CH_2$—$CH_2$—OH   butan-1-ol, a primary alcohol

$CH_3$—$CH_2$—CH—$CH_3$ with OH below   butan-2-ol, a secondary alcohol

$CH_3$—C($CH_3$)—$CH_3$ with OH below   2-methylpropan-2-ol, a tertiary alcohol

**15.02   Names and structures of alcohols**

are far less volatile than their equivalent hydrocarbons. For the same reason, alcohols with relatively short hydrocarbon chains mix freely with water.

## Chemical properties

*The reactions with sodium and with $PCl_5$ can both help to identify —OH groups in molecules because they both produce gases with distinct properties.*

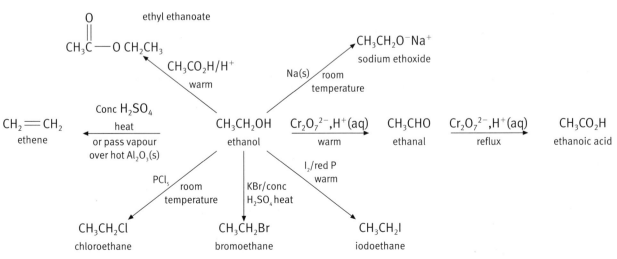

**15.01   Reactions of ethanol**

**Esters** are the fruity compounds that contribute to the flavour of bananas, pineapples and many other fruits. The smell of esters contributes to the scent of perfumes. Fats and vegetable oils are esters. The general formula for an ester is

$$R—C\begin{matrix}O\\ \\O—R'\end{matrix}$$

where R and R' are alkyl groups.

primary alcohol $\xrightarrow[\text{warm}]{Cr_2O_7^{2-},H^+(aq)}$ aldehyde

$\xrightarrow[\text{reflux}]{\text{excess } Cr_2O_7^{2-},H^+(aq)}$ carboxylic acid

secondary alcohol $\xrightarrow[\text{reflux}]{Cr_2O_7^{2-},H^+(aq)}$ ketone

tertiary alcohol → no reaction

**15.03 Use of oxidation with an acidified solution of dichromate(VI) ions to distinguish primary, secondary and tertiary alcohols**

> ℹ **The symbol [O] is a shorthand way of balancing the equation. [O] represents the oxygen atoms from the oxidising agent.**

Oxidation reactions distinguish primary alcohols, secondary alcohols and tertiary alcohols.

**Distinguishing aldehydes and ketones**

Fehling's solution and Tollens reagent distinguish aldehydes (from a primary alcohol) and ketones (from a secondary alcohol). Both test reagents are oxidising agents that change colour as they oxidise an aldehyde to a carboxylic acid. Neither reagent will oxidise ketones.

Fehling's solution contains an alkaline solution of complex copper(II) ions. On warming with an aldehyde the deep blue solution turns greenish and then loses its blue colour as an orange-red precipitate of copper(I) oxide appears.

Tollens reagent also gives a positive result with aldehydes but not with ketones. A shiny silver mirror forms on the glass of a clean test tube on warming the reagent with an aldehyde.

Reducing agents will reverse the oxidation of aldehydes and ketones. A suitable reducing agent is sodium tetrahydridoborate(III), $NaBH_4$, in aqueous solution.

Infra-red spectra can help to distinguish the functional groups in the products of the oxidation reactions of alcohols (Figure 15.04).

In the elimination of water from an alcohol, the acid acts as a catalyst. The first step of the mechanism is that the —OH group of the alcohol acts as a base accepting a proton, $H^+$, from the acid. This means that when the C—O bond breaks, the leaving group is a water molecule rather than a hydroxide ion. The formation of an alkene follows as the intermediate carbocation loses a proton (Figure 15.05).

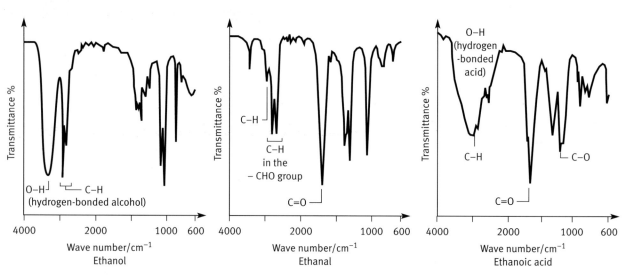

**15.04 Infra-red spectra for ethanol and its oxidation products**

**15.05 Mechanism for the elimination of water from an alcohol**

## Definition

A **leaving group** is an atom or molecule that breaks away from a molecule during a reaction.

## TEST YOURSELF

2 Write an equation for the reaction of water with sodium and compare it with the reaction of ethanol with sodium. What gas is formed and how could you identify the gas?

3 What gas is given off when $PCl_5$ reacts with an alcohol. What tests can be used to identify the gas?

4 Is it the C—O or the O—H bond that breaks when an alcohol reacts with:
   a sodium
   b $PCl_5$
   c concentrated sulfuric acid.

5 Write the balanced equation for converting propan-1-ol to each of the named products. State the conditions for reaction.
   a 1-iodopropane
   b propene
   c propanal
   d propyl ethanoate.

6 Write the equation for the reduction of butanal to butan-1-ol by $NaBH_4$. Represent the hydrogen from the reducing agent as [H].

## Manufacture and uses of alcohols

Ethanol is the alcohol in beer, wine and spirits. Alcohols are useful solvents in the home, in laboratories and in industry.

Methanol and ethanol are both useful fuels.

The chemical industry makes ethanol by hydrating ethene in the presence of an acid catalyst.

An alternative source of alcohol is fermentation, which converts sugars to ethanol and carbon dioxide. This is an example of anaerobic respiration. Fermentation is catalysed by an enzyme from yeast.

$$C_6H_{12}O_6(aq) \rightarrow 2CO_2(g) + 2C_2H_5OH(aq)$$
   glucose        carbon dioxide        ethanol

Ethanol is a useful solvent. Methylated spirit is ethanol with about 5% methanol to make it undrinkable. Industrial methylated spirit is used as a solvent commercially and in laboratories. Surgical spirit is industrial methylated spirit with other additives including castor oil.

## TEST YOURSELF

7 Write the equation and give the conditions for the industrial manufacture of ethanol from ethene (see page 90).

8 Write an equation for the complete combustion of methanol.

## REVIEW

Add to your collection of revision cards to learn the organic reactions of alcohols (see page 81). Extend your Mind Map of organic chemistry (see page 76) by adding more about:

• **the reactions of alcohols.**

## Oil refining

Crude oil is the main source of fuels and organic compounds. Oil refining starts with fractional distillation. This is the first stage in the production of fuels and petrochemicals.

> **i** *Crude oil consists mainly of alkane hydrocarbons.*

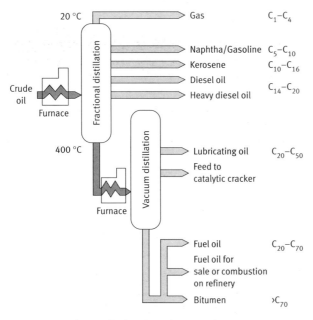

**16.01   Fractional distillation of crude oil**

## Fractional distillation

The fractional distillation column is hotter at the bottom and cooler at the top. Rising vapour condenses when it reaches the tray with liquid at a temperature below its boiling point.

Hydrocarbons with small molecules rise to the top of the column while larger molecules stay at the bottom.

Vacuum distillation separates the components of crude oil with boiling points too high for them to vaporise at atmospheric pressure. Lowering the pressure in a separate column reduces the boiling points of the hydrocarbons and makes distillation possible.

Oil refineries have to produce the various oil products in the quantities needed by industrial and domestic users. Generally, crude oil contains too much of the high-boiling fractions with bigger molecules and not enough of the low-boiling fractions with smaller molecules needed for fuels such as petrol.

## Fuels from oil

Petrol is a blend of hydrocarbons based on the gasoline fraction (hydrocarbons with 5–10 carbon atoms). Fuels have to be refined to remove components, such as sulfur compounds, which would harm engines or cause air pollution when they burn.

### Definition

**Energy density** is the amount of energy available from a kilogram of fuel. This is especially important for fuels used for transport. The energy density of hexane (a hydrocarbon in petrol) is 48 400 kJ kg$^{-1}$. Ethanol, an alternative fuel used on its own, or in gasohol, has an energy density of only 29 700 kJ kg$^{-1}$.

For smooth running the petrol has to burn smoothly without knocking. The octane number of a fuel measures its performance. The higher the compression of fuel and air in the engine cylinders, the higher the octane number has to be to stop knocking.

### Definition

**Knocking** is a noise from a petrol engine heard when the mixture of fuel and air ignites too early while still being compressed by the piston. This is pre-ignition. Knocking is a sign that a fuel with a higher octane number is needed.

Anti-knock additives used to be lead compounds. Leaded fuel is now being phased out and the oil companies produce high-octane fuel by increasing the proportions of both branched alkanes and arenes; they may also blend in some oxygen compounds. The four main approaches are cracking, isomerisation, reforming and adding oxygen compounds, such as alcohols and ethers.

# Cracking

Catalytic cracking converts heavier fractions, such as diesel oil or fuel oil, from the fractional distillation of crude oil into more useful hydrocarbons for fuels by breaking up larger molecules into smaller ones.

Cracking converts the longer chain alkanes with a dozen or more carbon atoms into smaller molecules, which are a mixture of branched alkanes, cycloalkanes, alkenes and branched alkenes.

The catalyst is a zeolite. Zeolites have a three-dimensional structure in which the silicon and oxygen atoms form tunnels and cavities into which small molecules can fit.

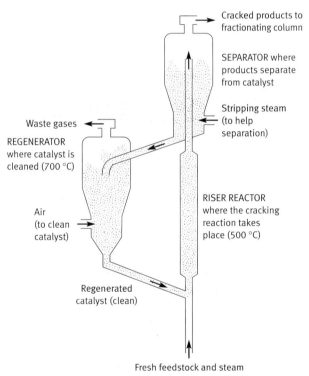

**16.02 Catalytic cracking. The catalyst powder flows to the vertical reactor where cracking takes place. The cracked vapours pass to a fractionating column while the catalyst flows to the regenerator**

> **i** *Catalytic cracking takes place on the surface of the catalyst, which is polar, and causes the bonds to break, forming ionic intermediates.*

## Isomerisation

Isomerisation turns straight chain alkanes into branched chain compounds by passing them over a platinum catalyst. Typically, compounds such as pentane are changed into branched isomers such as 2-methylbutane. The value of the process is that branched alkanes increase the octane number of petrol.

## Reforming

Reforming converts alkanes to arenes (aromatic hydrocarbons) such as benzene and methylbenzene. It can also convert alkanes to cyclic alkanes.

The catalyst for this process is often one or more of the precious metals, such as platinum and rhodium, supported on an inert material such as aluminium oxide. The process operates at about 500 °C.

$$CH_3CH_2CH_2CH_2CH_2CH_2CH_3 \xrightarrow[\text{heat, pressure}]{\text{Pt catalyst}} \text{methylbenzene} + 4H_2(g)$$

heptane

$$\text{cyclohexane} \xrightarrow[\text{heat, pressure}]{\text{Pt catalyst}} \text{benzene} + 3H_2(g)$$

**16.03 Example of reforming**

## Adding oxygen compounds

Alcohols and ethers such as MTBE (initials based on its older name methyl tertiary butyl ether now called 2-methoxy-2-methylpropane) can also help to raise the octane number of petrol.

# Chemicals from oil

Crude oil is also a valuable source of chemicals, especially alkenes, which are building blocks for the synthesis of new chemicals.

## Steam (thermal) cracking

Steam cracking converts hydrocarbons to alkenes. It converts ethane to ethene.

A mixture of the hydrocarbon vapour and steam passes under pressure through tubes in a furnace where they are heated to about 1000 °C. So this is thermal cracking as opposed to catalytic cracking.

**By the end of this topic you will be able to:**

✔ **select a suitable experimental method for following the rate of a reaction**

✔ **explain and use the terms 'rate of reaction', 'order' and 'rate constant'**

✔ **recall that the half-life of a first order reaction is independent of concentration**

✔ **work out rates of reaction and half-lives from concentration-time graphs**

✔ **recognise the rate-concentration graphs for zero, first and second order reactions**

✔ **use the initial-rate method to deduce the order of a reaction with respect to a reactant**

✔ **calculate a rate constant from a rate equation**

✔ **describe qualitatively the effect of temperature on a rate constant (with the help of the Arrhenius equation)**

✔ **explain the term 'rate-determining step' and show how the form of the rate equation can help to deduce the mechanism of a reaction.**

## Investigating reaction rates

Chemists measure rates of reaction by measuring the rate of formation of a product or the rate of removal of a reactant.

The usual procedure for finding rates is to measure some property of the reaction mixture, such as its volume, and to see how this property varies with time.

$$\text{Rate} = \frac{\text{change in the measured property}}{\text{time}}$$

Rates are measured in practical units, such as 'cm per second', and then converted to mol s$^{-1}$ or mol dm$^{-3}$ s$^{-1}$ if necessary.

Methods for studying rates include:

- collecting and measuring the volume of a gas formed

- removing measured samples of the mixture, stopping the reaction and then determining the concentration of one reactant or product by titration

- using a colorimeter to follow the formation of a coloured product or the removal of a coloured reactant

- using a conductivity cell and meter to measure the changes in electrical conductivity of the reaction mixture and the number or nature of the ion changes.

> **i** *Concentration-time graphs display the results from rate experiments. The gradient of a concentration-time graph at a given point measures the rate of reaction at that time (see Figure 10.01 on page 63).*

**TEST YOURSELF**

1 **Suggest a practical method for measuring the rate of each of these reactions:**

  a $Mg(s) + 2HCl(aq) \rightarrow MgCl_2(aq) + H_2(g)$

  b $CH_3COCH_3(aq) + I_2(aq)$
         $\rightarrow CH_3COCH_2I(aq) + H^+(aq) + I^-(aq)$

  c $CH_3CO_2C_2H_5(l) + H_2O(l)$
         $\rightarrow CH_3CO_2H(aq) + C_2H_5OH(aq)$

  d $C_4H_9I(l) + H_2O(l)$
         $\rightarrow C_4H_9OH(aq) + H^+(aq) + I^-(aq)$

## Rate equations

### Reaction orders

Rate equations sum up the results of investigations into the rates of reaction.

Consider a general reaction in which the equation shows that x mol of A reacts with y mol of B to form products:

$xA + yB \rightarrow$ products

Experimental results show that the rate of reaction can be described by a rate equation:

$\text{Rate} = k[A]^n[B]^m$

> **i** *Do not forget that [X] means the concentration of X in mol dm$^{-3}$.*

The powers n and m are the reaction orders. This reaction is order n with respect to A and order m with respect to B. The overall order of the reaction is (m + n)

The constant, $k$, is the rate constant.

> **i** *Note that n and m in the rate equation cannot be deduced from the values of x and y in the balanced equation. Rate equations can only be found by experiment.*

The units of a rate constant depend on the overall order of reaction.

| Overall order | Units of the rate constant |
|---|---|
| zero | $mol\ dm^{-3}\ s^{-1}$ |
| first | $s^{-1}$ |
| second | $mol^{-1}\ dm^3\ s^{-1}$ |
| third | $mol^{-2}\ dm^6\ s^{-1}$ |

### WORKED EXAMPLE

The decomposition of $N_2O_5$ to $NO_2$ and $O_2$ is a first order reaction. The rate of decomposition in a solution of an organic solvent is $2.10 \times 10^{-5}\ mol\ dm^{-3}s^{-1}$ when the concentration of $N_2O_5$ is $2.00\ mol\ dm^{-3}$. What is the value of the rate constant?

### Answer

Rate $= k \times [N_2O_5]$

Hence $k = $ rate $\div [N_2O_5]$

$k = 2.10 \times 10^{-5}\ mol\ dm^{-3}s^{-1} \div 2.00\ mol\ dm^{-3}$

$k = 1.05 \times 10^{-5}\ s^{-1}$

### Zero order

A reaction is zero order with respect to a reactant if the rate of reaction is unaffected by changes in the concentration of that reactant. The concentration term for this reactant is raised to the power zero in the *rate equation*.

Rate $= k[X]^0 = k$ (a constant) since $[X]^0 = 1$

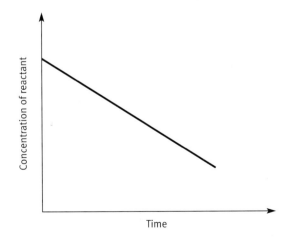

**18.01  Variation of concentration of a reactant plotted against time for a zero order reaction. The gradient of this graph measures the rate of reaction. The gradient is a constant, so the rate stays the same even though the concentration of the reactant is falling**

 *Any term raised to the power zero equals 1.*

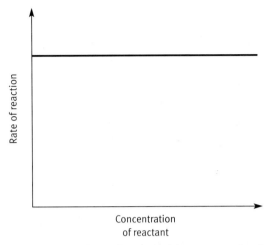

**18.02  Variation of reaction rate with concentration for a zero order reaction**

### First order

A reaction is first order with respect to a reactant if the rate of reaction is proportional to the concentration of that reactant. The concentration term for this reactant is raised to the power one in the rate equation.

Rate $= k[X]^1 = k[X]$

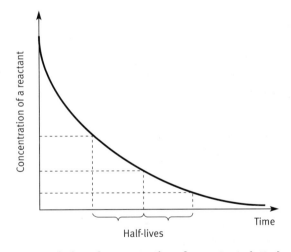

**18.03  Variation of concentration of a reactant plotted against time for a first order reaction. At a constant temperature, the half-life of a first order reaction is the same wherever it is measured on a concentration-time graph. So the half-life is independent of the initial concentration**

 *The half-life of a reaction is the time for the concentration of one of the reactants to fall by half. Half-lives help to identify first order reactions.*

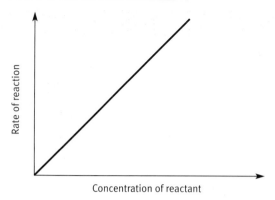

**18.04 Variation of reaction rate with concentration for a first order reaction. The graph is a straight line through the origin showing that the rate is proportional to the concentration of the reactant**

## Second order reaction

A reaction is second order with respect to a reactant if the rate of reaction is proportional to the concentration of that reactant squared. The concentration term for this reactant is raised to the power two in the rate equation. At its simplest, the rate equation for a second order reaction is:

Rate $= k[X]^2$

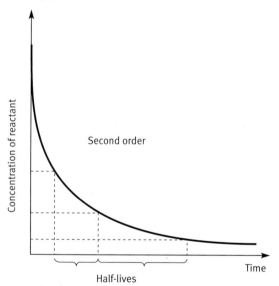

**18.05 Variation of concentration of a reactant plotted against time for a second order reaction. The half-life for a second order reaction is not a constant. The time for the concentration to fall from c to c/2 is half the time for the concentration to fall from c/2 to c/4. The half-life is inversely proportional to the starting concentration**

## Determining reaction orders

It is possible to recognise a first order reaction by showing that the half-life for the concentration-time graph is a constant (see Figure 18.03). In most other instances the method for finding the reaction orders is the initial rate method.

The initial rate method is based on finding the rate immediately after the start of a reaction. This is the one point when all the concentrations are known.

The procedure is to make up a series of mixtures in which all the initial concentrations are the same except one. A suitable method is used to measure the change of concentration with time for each mixture. The results are used to plot concentration-time graphs. The initial rate for each mixture is then found by drawing tangents to the curve at the start and calculating their gradients.

## WORKED EXAMPLE

The initial rate method was used to study the reaction:

$O_2(g) + 2NO(g) \rightarrow 2NO_2(g)$

The initial rate was calculated from five graphs plotted to show how the concentration of $NO_2$ varied with time for different initial concentrations of reactants (see table below).

What is:

a   the rate equation for the reaction?

b   the value of the rate constant?

### Notes on the method

Recall that the rate equation cannot be worked out from the balanced equation for the reaction.

First study the experiments in which the concentration of $O_2$ varies but the concentration of NO stays the same. How does doubling or tripling the concentration of $O_2$ affect the rate?

Next study the experiments in which the concentration of NO varies but the concentration of $O_2$ stays the same. How does doubling the concentration of NO affect the rate?

Substitute values for any one experiment in the rate equation to find the value of the rate constant, $k$. Take care with the units.

### Answer

From experiments 1, 2 and 3: doubling $[O_2]_{initial}$ increases the rate by a factor of 2. Tripling $[O_2]_{initial}$ increases the rate by a factor of 3 . So rate $\propto [O_2]$.

From experiments 3, 4 and 5: doubling $[NO]_{initial}$ increases the rate by a factor of 4 ($= 2^2$). Tripling $[NO]_{initial}$ increases the rate by a factor of 9 ($= 3^2$) . So rate $\propto [NO]^2$ .

The reaction is first order with respect to $O_2$ and second order with respect to NO. The rate equation is:

rate $= k\,[O_2][NO]^2$

Rearranging this equation, and substituting values from experiment 1:

$$k = \frac{rate}{[O_2][NO]^2}$$

$$k = \frac{7 \times 10^{-6}\ mol\ dm^{-3}\ s^{-1}}{0.001\ mol\ dm^{-3} \times (0.001\ mol\ dm^{-3})^2}$$

$k = 7 \times 10^3\ mol^{-2}\ dm^6\ s^{-1}$

| Experiment | Initial concentration of $O_2$/mol dm$^{-3}$ | Initial concentration of NO/mol dm$^{-3}$ | Initial rate of reaction/mol dm$^{-3}$ s$^{-1}$ |
| --- | --- | --- | --- |
| 1 | 0.001 | 0.001 | $7 \times 10^{-6}$ |
| 2 | 0.002 | 0.001 | $14 \times 10^{-6}$ |
| 3 | 0.003 | 0.001 | $21 \times 10^{-6}$ |
| 4 | 0.003 | 0.002 | $84 \times 10^{-6}$ |
| 5 | 0.003 | 0.003 | $189 \times 10^{-6}$ |

### Factfile

**Mole fraction**

A way of measuring the proportion of a substance in a mixture where it is the amounts in moles that matter and not the chemical nature of the components.

In a mixture of $n_A$ moles of A with $n_B$ moles of B and $n_C$ moles of C, the mole fractions (symbol $X$) are given by the following:

$$X_A = \frac{n_A}{n_A + n_B + n_C}$$

$$X_B = \frac{n_B}{n_A + n_B + n_C}$$

$$X_C = \frac{n_C}{n_A + n_B + n_C}$$

So the mole fraction of B is the fraction of all the moles that are moles of B.

The sum of all the mole fractions is 1, so

$$X_A + X_B + X_C = 1$$

### TEST YOURSELF

4  Phosphorus pentachloride decomposes into phosphorus trichloride and chlorine on heating. Heating a 0.5 mol sample of $PCl_5$ to a certain constant temperature produced an equilibrium mixture of the three gases at a total pressure of 200 kPa in which there was 0.2 mol $PCl_5$.

   Calculate the value of $K_p$ under these conditions.

5  At 373 K and 200 kPa pressure, an equilibrium mixture of gases consisted of 0.994 mol carbon dioxide, 0.994 mol hydrogen, 0.0062 mol carbon monoxide and 0.0062 mol steam. Calculate the value of $K_p$ for the reaction between carbon dioxide and hydrogen.

### WORKED EXAMPLE

When a mixture of 0.120 mol sulfur dioxide and 0.115 mol oxygen comes to equilibrium at a certain temperature and a total pressure of 540 kPa, the amount of sulfur trioxide formed is 0.07 mol. Calculate $K_p$ for the reaction.

#### Notes on the method

First write the equation for the reaction and work out the amount in moles of each gas at equilibrium. Note that 2 mol $SO_2(g)$ reacts with 1 mol $O_2(g)$ forming 2 mol $SO_3(g)$.

Hence calculate the mole fraction of each gas. This leads to the partial pressures for the gases at equilibrium. Substitute these values in the expression for $K_p$ and then decide on the units.

#### Answer

| | $2SO_2(g)$ | $+$ | $O_2(g)$ | $2SO_3(g)$ |
|---|---|---|---|---|
| The equation: | $2SO_2(g)$ | $+$ | $O_2(g)$ | $2SO_3(g)$ |
| Initial amounts | 0.120 mol | | 0.115 mol | 0.00 mol |
| Equilibrium amount | 0.050 mol | | 0.080 mol | 0.070 mol |
| Equilibrium mole fractions | $\frac{0.05}{0.2}$ | | $\frac{0.08}{0.2}$ | $\frac{0.07}{0.2}$ |
| Equilibrium partial pressures | $\frac{0.05}{0.2} \times 540$ kPa | | $\frac{0.08}{0.2} \times 540$ kPa | $\frac{0.07}{0.2} \times 540$ kPa |
| | $= 135$ kPa | | $= 216$ kPa | $= 189$ kPa |

Hence $K_p = \dfrac{(p_{SO_3})^2}{(p_{SO_2})^2 (p_{O_2})} = \dfrac{(189 \text{ kPa})^2}{(135 \text{ kPa})^2 (216 \text{ kPa})}$

$= 9.1 \text{ kPa}^{-1}$

## Heterogeneous equilibria

In some equilibrium systems not all the substances involved are in the same phase. An example is the equilibrium state involving two solids and a gas formed on heating calcium carbonate in a closed container.

$$CaCO_3(s) \rightleftharpoons CaO(s) + CO_2(g)$$

The concentrations of solids do not appear in the expression for the equilibrium constant. Pure solids have a constant 'concentration'.

$$K_c = [CO_2(g)] \quad \text{or} \quad K_p = p_{CO_2}$$

The same applies to the equilibrium between a solid and its saturated solution in water.

### Definition

Chemical systems often have more than one **phase**. Each phase is distinct but need not be pure.

A solid in equilibrium with its saturated solution is a two-phase system.

In the reactor for ammonia manufacture the mixture of nitrogen, hydrogen and ammonia gases is one gaseous phase with the iron catalyst being a separate solid phase.

### TEST YOURSELF

6 **Write the expression for $K_c$ for these equilibria:**

a **$3Fe(s) + 4H_2O(g) \rightleftharpoons Fe_3O_4(s) + 4H_2(g)$**

b **$Fe^{3+}(aq) + Ag(s) \rightleftharpoons Fe^{2+}(aq) + Ag^+(aq)$**

## Effects of changing conditions on equilibria

### Effect of changing concentration (or pressure)

The expression for $K_c$ or $K_p$ makes it possible to explain the effect of changing the concentration of one of the chemicals in an equilibrium mixture. In a solution of bromine in water:

$$\underbrace{Br_2(aq)}_{orange} + H_2O(l) \rightleftharpoons \underbrace{HOBr(aq) + Br^-(aq) + H^+(aq)}_{colourless}$$

At equilibrium: $K_c = \dfrac{[HOBr(aq)][Br^-(aq)][H^+(aq)]}{[Br_2(aq)]}$

where these are equilibrium concentrations.

*Note that in dilute aqueous solutions $[H_2O(l)]$ is constant and so does not appear in the expression for $K_c$.*

Adding alkali removes $H^+(aq)$ from the right hand side:

$$H^+(aq) + OH^-(aq) \rightarrow H_2O(l).$$

This briefly upsets the equilibrium. For an instant after adding alkali:

$$\frac{[HOBr(aq)][Br^-(aq)][H^+(aq)]}{[Br_2(aq)]} < K_c$$

The system restores equilibrium as bromine reacts with water to produce more of the products while lowering the concentration of $Br_2(aq)$. Very soon there is a new equilibrium. Once again:

$$\frac{[HOBr(aq)][Br^-(aq)][H^+(aq)]}{[Br_2(aq)]} = K_c$$

but now with new values for the various concentrations.

Speaking roughly, chemists say that adding alkali makes the 'position of equilibrium shift to the right'. This is as Le Chatelier's principle predicts (see Chapter 11). The advantage of using $K_c$ (or $K_p$ for pressure changes) is that it makes quantitative predictions possible.

*Remember that changing the concentration (or pressure) does not alter the value of the equilibrium constant if the temperature stays the same.*

### TEST YOURSELF

7 **Use the expression for the equilibrium constant to explain the effect of raising the pressure on these equilibria:**

a **$N_2(g) + 3H_2(g) \rightleftharpoons 2NH_3(g)$**

b **$H_2(g) + I_2(g) \rightleftharpoons 2HI(g)$**

### Effect of changing the temperature

The shift in the position of equilibrium happens when the temperature changes. The effect depends on the enthalpy change for the reaction. Le Chatelier's principle predicts that raising the temperature makes the equilibrium shift in the direction that is endothermic. In sulfuric acid manufacture, for example, raising the temperature lowers the percentage of sulfur dioxide at equilibrium.

$$2SO_2(g) + O_2(g) \rightleftharpoons 2SO_3(g) \quad \Delta H = -98 \text{ kJ mol}^{-1}$$

The equilibrium shifts to the left as the temperature rises because this is the direction in which the reaction is endothermic.

These shifts happen because equilibrium constants vary with temperature.

$$K_p = \frac{p_{SO_3}{}^2}{p_{SO_2}{}^2 p_{O_2}}$$

At 500 K, $K_p = 2.5 \times 10^{10}$ atm$^{-1}$, but at 700 K, $K_p = 3.0 \times 10^4$ atm$^{-1}$. The value of the equilibrium constant falls as the temperature rises. With a smaller value of $K_p$ the proportion of $SO_3(g)$ falls while the proportions of $SO_2(g)$ and $O_2(g)$ rise at equilibrium.

> **i** *The value of the equilibrium constant for an exothermic reaction decreases as the temperature rises.*

> **i** *The value of the equilibrium constant for an endothermic reaction rises as the temperature rises.*

## TEST YOURSELF

8   For the reaction of carbon dioxide with hydrogen to form steam and carbon monoxide the value of $K_p$ is $7.8 \times 10^{-3}$ at 500 K and 1.45 at 1100 K. What can you deduce from this information?

9   For the reaction of hydrogen with iodine vapour to form hydrogen iodide the value of $K_p$ is 160 at 500 K and 25 at 1100 K. What can you deduce from this information?

## REVIEW

Solving the 'test yourself' problems is the most effective way of revising the ideas in this topic. Check your answers against the solutions on page 176. Where you feel the need for more practice, look for more examples in past examination papers and text books.

**By the end of this topic you will be able to:**

✔ define acids and bases in terms of proton transfer, identify examples of acid-base equilibria and recognise acid-base conjugate pairs

✔ define pH, use the pH scale and calculate the pH of a solution of a strong acid given its molar concentration (and vice versa)

✔ use $K_w$ or $pK_w$ to calculate the pH of a solution of a strong base

✔ recall that weak acids and bases are only partially ionised in aqueous solution

✔ define $K_a$ and $pK_a$ and be able to calculate the pH of a weak acid given its molar concentration

✔ describe the shapes of the pH curves for acid-base titrations in all combinations of strong and weak monoprotic acids and bases

✔ determine the value for $K_a$ of a weak acid from a titration curve

✔ recall that indicators change colour over a narrow pH range and be able to select a suitable indicator for an acid-base titration given $pK$ indicator

✔ explain the action of buffer solutions (qualitatively and quantitatively) and calculate the pH of a buffer solution

✔ account for values for enthalpies of neutralisation in terms of the strength of the acids and bases involved.

## The Brønsted-Lowry theory

The Brønsted-Lowry theory describes acids as proton donors and bases as proton acceptors.

 *A proton is the nucleus of a hydrogen atom, so a hydrogen ion, $H^+$, is a proton.*

## Acids

According to the theory, hydrogen chloride molecules give protons (hydrogen ions) to water molecules when they dissolve in water, producing hydrated hydrogen ions called oxonium ions. The water accepts the proton and thus acts as a base.

$$HCl(g) + H_2O(l) \rightleftharpoons H_3O^+(aq) + Cl^-(aq)$$
acid  base

The oxonium ion is often abbreviated to $H^+(aq)$ and the above equation then simplifies to:

$$HCl(g) \rightleftharpoons H^+(aq) + Cl^-(aq)$$

Hydrogen chloride is an example of a strong acid, so this equilibrium is well over to the right. Strong acids are fully ionised in solution. Other examples of strong acids are nitric acid and sulfuric acid.

### Definition

A **monoprotic acid**: an acid that can give away (donate) one proton per molecule. Examples of monoprotic acids are hydrogen chloride, HCl, ethanoic acid, $CH_3CO_2H$, and nitric acid, $HNO_3$.

An example of an acid-base reaction that does not involve water is the formation of a white smoke of ammonium chloride when ammonia gas mixes with hydrogen chloride gas.

$$NH_3(g) + HCl(g) \rightleftharpoons NH_4^+Cl^-(s)$$
base  acid

## Bases

A base is a molecule or ion that can accept a hydrogen ion (proton) from an acid. A base has a lone pair of electrons that can form a dative covalent bond with a proton.

**20.01  A hydroxide ion has a lone pair of electrons that can form a dative covalent bond with a hydrogen ion**

Common bases are the oxide and hydroxide ions, ammonia, amines and the carbonate and hydrogencarbonate ions. There is a lone pair on the nitrogen atom of ammonia that allows it to act as a base:

$$NH_3(g) + HNO_3(g) \rightarrow NH_4^+NO_3^-(s)$$
base  acid

## Conjugate acid-base pairs

Any acid-base equilibrium involves a competition for protons.

$$NH_4^+(aq) + H_2O(l) \rightleftharpoons NH_3(aq) + H_3O^+(aq)$$

acid 1       base 2       base 1       acid 2

On the left-hand side of the equation the protons are held by lone pairs on the ammonia molecules. On the right-hand side they are held by lone pairs on water molecules.

The equilibrium involves two conjugate acid-base pairs:

- $NH_4^+$ and $NH_3$ and
- $H_3O^{+\cdot}$ and $H_2O$.

> **i** *An acid turns into its conjugate base when it loses a proton. A base turns into its conjugate acid when it gains a proton.*

### TEST YOURSELF

1. **Show that the reactions between these pairs of compounds are acid-base reactions and identify as precisely as possible the molecules or ions that are the acid and the base in each example.**
   a   $CuO + H_2SO_4$
   b   $HNO_3 + NH_3$
   c   $NH_4NO_3 + NaOH$
   d   $HCl + Na_2CO_3$

2. **Identify and name the conjugate base of these acids: $HNO_3$, $CH_3CO_2H$, $H_2SO_4$, $HCO_3^-$**

3. **Identify the conjugate acid of these bases: $OH^-$, $NH_3$, $HCO_3^-$**

## pH

The pH scale is a logarithmic scale for measuring the concentration of aqueous hydrogen ions in solutions.

$$pH = -\log [H_3O^+(aq)] \text{ or } pH = -\log [H^+(aq)]$$

### The ionic product of water, $K_w$

There are hydrogen and hydroxide ions even in pure water because of a transfer of hydrogen ions between water molecules. This only happens to a very slight extent.

$$H_2O(l) + H_2O(l) \rightleftharpoons H_3O^+(aq) + OH^-(aq)$$

which can be written more simply as:

$$H_2O(l) \rightleftharpoons H^+(aq) + OH^-(aq)$$

### WORKED EXAMPLE

What is the pH of 0.02 mol dm$^{-3}$ nitric acid?

#### Notes on the method

Nitric acid is a strong acid so it is fully ionised. Note that 1 mol $HNO_3$ gives 1 mol $H^+(aq)$.

Use the log button on your calculator. Do not forget the minus sign in the definition of pH.

#### Answer

$[H^+(aq)] = 0.02$ mol dm$^{-3}$
$pH = -\log (0.02) = 1.7$

The equilibrium constant, $K_c = \dfrac{[H^+(aq)][OH^-(aq)]}{[H_2O(l)]}$

There is such a large excess of water that $[H_2O(l)]$ is a constant, so the relationship simplifies to:

$K_w = [H^+(aq)][OH^-(aq)]$

where $K_w$ is the ionic product of water.

The pH of pure water is 7. So the hydrogen ion concentration at equilibrium:
$[H^+(aq)] = 10^{-7}$ mol dm$^{-3}$.

Also in pure water $[H_3O^+(aq)] = [OH^-(aq)]$

so the $[OH^-(aq)] = 10^{-7}$ mol dm$^{-3}$.

Hence $K_w = 10^{-14}$ mol$^2$ dm$^{-6}$

$K_w$ is a constant in all aqueous solutions at 298 K. This makes it possible to calculate the pH of alkalis.

## WORKED EXAMPLE

What is the aqueous hydrogen ion concentration of a solution with pH 4.6?

### Notes on the method

$pH = -\log [H^+(aq)]$

From the definition of logarithms this rearranges to $[H^+(aq)] = 10^{-pH}$

Use the inverse log button ($10^x$) on your calculator. Do not forget the minus sign in the definition of pH.

### Answer

$pH = 4.6$
$[H^+(aq)] = 10^{-4.6} = 2.5 \times 10^{-5}$ mol dm$^{-3}$

## WORKED EXAMPLE

What is the pH of a 0.05 mol dm$^{-3}$ solution of sodium hydroxide?

### Notes on the method

Sodium hydroxide is fully ionised in solution. So in this solution $[OH^-(aq)] = 0.05$ mol dm$^{-3}$

$pH = -\log [H^+(aq)]$

### Answer

For this solution:

$K_w = [H^+(aq)] \times 0.05$ mol dm$^{-3}$ $= 10^{-14}$ mol$^2$ dm$^{-6}$

So $[H^+(aq)] = \dfrac{10^{-14} \text{ mol}^2 \text{ dm}^{-6}}{0.05 \text{ mol dm}^{-3}}$

$= 2 \times 10^{-13}$ mol dm$^{-3}$

Hence $pH = -\log (2 \times 10^{-13}) = 12.7$

## Working in logarithms

The logarithmic form of equilibrium constants is particularly useful for pH calculations. Taking logarithms produces a convenient small scale of values.

### Definition

$pK_w = -\log K_w$

---

$K_w = [H^+][OH^-] = 10^{-14}$ at 298 K

Taking logarithms gives:

$\log K_w = \log[H^+] + \log[OH^-] = \log 10^{-14} = -14$

Multiplying through by $-1$, reverses the signs:

$-\log K_w = -\log [H^+] - \log[OH^-] = 14$

Hence: $pK_w = pH + pOH = 14$, where pOH is defined as $-\log[OH^-]$ by analogy with pH.

> **i** *So, pH = 14 − pOH, which makes it easy to calculate the pH of alkaline solutions.*

## WORKED EXAMPLE

What is the pH of a 0.05 mol dm$^{-3}$ solution of sodium hydroxide?

### Notes on the method

Sodium hydroxide, NaOH, is a strong base so it is fully ionised.

Find the values of logarithms with a calculator.

### Answer

$[OH^-] = 0.05$ mol dm$^{-3}$

$pOH = -\log 0.05 = 1.3$

$pH = 14 - pOH = 14 - 1.3 = 12.7$

### TEST YOURSELF

4  What are the hydrogen ion concentrations in solutions with these pH values?

   a  2.0

   b  3.7

   c  9.2

5  Calculate the pH of these solutions:

   a  0.1 mol dm$^{-3}$ HCl

   b  0.005 mol dm$^{-3}$ HNO$_3$

   c  1.0 mol dm$^{-3}$ NaOH

   d  0.02 mol dm$^{-3}$ KOH.

6  Calculate the concentration of OH$^-$ ions in:

   a  0.1 mol dm$^{-3}$ NaOH

   b  0.1 mol dm$^{-3}$ HCl

## Weak acids and bases

### Weak acids

Weak acids are only slightly ionised when they dissolve in water. In a 0.1 mol dm$^{-3}$ solution of ethanoic acid, for example, only about one in a hundred molecules reacts with water to form oxonium ions.

### Definitions

Acid **strength** is the degree of ionisation.

**Concentration** is the amount of acid in a litre, mol dm$^{-3}$.

Acid dissociation constants are equilibrium constants that show the extent to which acids dissociate into ions in solution.

For a weak acid represented by the formula HA:

$$HA(aq) + H_2O(l) \rightleftharpoons H_3O^+(aq) + A^-(aq)$$

According to the equilibrium law, the equilibrium

constant, $K_c = \dfrac{[H_3O^+(aq)][A^-(aq)]}{[HA(aq)][H_2O(l)]}$

In dilute solution the concentration of water is effectively constant, so the expression can be written in this form:

$$K_a = \frac{[H_3O^+(aq)][A^-(aq)]}{[HA(aq)]}$$

where $K_a$ is the acid dissociation constant.

> **i** *It takes just as much sodium hydroxide to neutralise 25 cm³ of 0.1 mol dm⁻³ of a weak acid, such as ethanoic acid, as it does to neutralise 25 cm³ of 0.1 mol dm⁻³ of a strong acid, such a hydrochloric acid.*

> **i** *The pH of a solution of acid alone does not show whether or not the acid is strong or weak. A solution of an acid with pH 4 might be a very dilute solution of a strong acid or a concentrated solution of a weak acid.*

### WORKED EXAMPLE

Calculate the hydrogen ion concentration and the pH of a 0.01 mol dm$^{-3}$ solution of propanoic acid. $K_a$ for the acid is $1.3 \times 10^{-5}$ mol dm$^{-3}$.

### Notes on the method

Two approximations simplify the calculation.

1. The first assumption is that $[H_3O^+(aq)] = [A^-(aq)]$. In this example A$^-$ is the propanoate ion $C_2H_5CO_2^-$. This assumption seems obvious from the equation for the ionisation of a weak acid but it ignores the hydrogen ions from the ionisation of water. Water produces far fewer hydrogen ions than most weak acids so its ionisation can be ignored.

2. The second assumption is that so little of the propanoic acid ionises in water that $[HA(aq)] \approx 0.01$ mol dm$^{-3}$. Here HA represents propanoic acid. This is a riskier assumption which has to be checked because in very dilute solutions the degree of ionisation may become quite large relative to the amount of acid in the solution. The more dilute the solution, the greater the degree of ionisation of the acid.

### Answer

$$K_a = \frac{[H_3O^+(aq)][A^-(aq)]}{[HA(aq)]}$$

$$= \frac{[H_3O^+(aq)]^2}{0.01 \text{ mol dm}^{-3}} = 1.3 \times 10^{-5} \text{ mol dm}^{-3}$$

Therefore $[H_3O^+(aq)]^2 = 1.3 \times 10^{-7}$ mol$^2$ dm$^{-6}$

So $[H_3O^+(aq)] = 3.6 \times 10^{-4}$ mol dm$^{-3}$

pH $= -\log[H_3O^+(aq)] = -\log(3.6 \times 10^{-4}) = 3.4$

Check the second assumption: in this case about 0.0004 mol dm$^{-3}$ of the 0.0100 mol dm$^{-3}$ of acid (4%) has ionised. In this instance the degree of ionisation is just about small enough to justify the assumption that $[HA(aq)]$ is approximately equal to the concentration of unionised acid.

### Definition

**p$K$**: the logarithmic form of an equilibrium constant that is particularly useful for *pH* calculations. Taking logarithms produces a convenient small scale of values. $pK_a = -\log K_a$

## Working in logarithms

Rearranging the expression for $K_a$ of a weak acid and then putting both sides of the equation into logarithmic form produces an equation that can be easily used to calculate pH values.

 *The stronger the acid the smaller the value of $pK_a$.*

$$K_a = \frac{[H_3O^+(aq)][A^-(aq)]}{[HA(aq)]}$$

Taking logs and substituting pH for $-\log[H_3O^+(aq)]$ and $pK_a$ for $-\log K_a$, gives:

$$pH = pK_a + \log\frac{[A^-(aq)]}{[HA(aq)]}$$

because $-\log\dfrac{[HA(aq)]}{[A^-(aq)]} = +\log\dfrac{[A^-(aq)]}{[HA(aq)]}$

This logarithmic form of the equilibrium law is particularly helpful when it comes to explaining the behaviour of indicators and buffer solutions.

In a mixture of a weak acid and its salt, the weak acid is only slightly ionised while the salt is fully ionised, so it is often accurate enough to assume that all the anions, $A^-(aq)$, come from the salt present and all the un-ionised molecules, $HA(aq)$, come from the acid.

Hence: $pH = pK_a + \log\dfrac{[salt]}{[acid]}$

## Weak bases

Weak bases are similarly only slightly ionised when they dissolve in water. In a 0.1 mol dm$^{-3}$ solution of ammonia, for example, only about one in a hundred molecules reacts with water to form ammonium ions.

$$NH_3(g) + H_2O(aq) \rightleftharpoons NH_4^+(aq) + OH^-(aq)$$

As with weak acids, it is important to distinguish between strength and concentration.

## Acid-base titrations

### Titration curves

Plotting a graph of pH against volume of alkali added during an acid-base titration gives a shape determined by the nature of the acid and the base.

The indicator chosen to detect the end-point must change colour completely in the pH range of the near vertical part of the curve.

Note that at the equivalence point, when exactly equal amounts of acid and base have been added, the pH is not always neutral.

Half way to the end-point, during the titration of a weak acid with a strong base, $pH = pK_a$. This follows from the logarithmic form of the equilibrium law.

$$pH = pK_a + \log\frac{[salt]}{[acid]}$$

Half way to the end-point, half of the weak acid has been neutralised and converted to its salt, so that:

$[salt] = [acid]$. This means that $pH = pK_a$ because $\log 1 = \log 10^0 = 0$.

### TEST YOURSELF

7 Calculate the pH of a 0.1 mol dm$^{-3}$ solution of methanoic acid given that $K_a = 1.6 \times 10^{-4}$ mol dm$^{-3}$.

8 What is the pH of a solution of white vinegar that contains 0.6% by mass of ethanoic acid given that $K_a = 1.7 \times 10^{-5}$ mol dm$^{-3}$?

9 What is the pH of a 0.01 mol dm$^{-3}$ solution of phenol given that $K_a = 1.28 \times 10^{-10}$ mol dm$^{-3}$?

10 a Arrange these acids in order of acid strength putting the strongest first:
carbonic acid, $pK_a = 6.4$
chlorethanoic acid, $pK_a = 2.9$
ethanoic acid, $pK_a = 4.8$
phenol, $pK_a = 9.9$
b Which of the acids will produce carbon dioxide gas when added to a solution of sodium hydrogencarbonate?

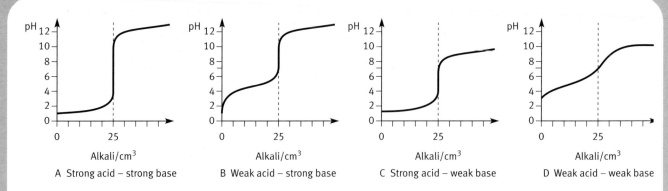

20.02    A, B, C and D graphs show the pH change on adding 0.1 mol dm$^{-3}$ of the named alkali to 25 cm$^3$ of a 0.1 mol dm$^{-3}$ named acid. Note the sharp change of pH around the equivalence point except when both the acid and the base are weak

### TEST YOURSELF

**11 Match these pairs of acids and bases with the four graphs, A, B, C and D, in Figure 20.02.**

   **a   HCO$_2$H—NaOH**

   **b   HNO$_3$—NH$_3$**

   **c   HCl—KOH**

   **d   CH$_3$CO$_2$H—NH$_3$**

**12 Why does the curve in graph B in Figure 20.02 end at a higher pH value than the curve in graph C?**

**13 Use graph B, Figure 20.02, to estimate p$K_a$ and, hence, $K_a$ for the weak acid.**

**14 Explain why the pH is not 7 at the equivalence point for a titration of a weak acid with a strong base.**

## Indicators

Acid-base indicators show up changes in pH of solutions. Indicators are weak acids or bases that change colour when they lose or gain hydrogen ions. When added to a solution, an indicator gains or loses protons depending on the pH of the solution. It is conventional to represent a weak acid indicator as HIn where In is a shorthand for the rest of the molecule. In water:

HIn(aq) + H$_2$O(l) $\rightleftharpoons$ H$_3$O$^+$(aq) + In$^-$(aq)

| un-ionised indicator | indicator after losing a proton |
|---|---|
| colour 1 | colour 2 |

Adding only a drop of indicator makes sure that there is not enough to affect the pH of the solution. The indicator equilibrium shifts according to the pH of the solution in which it finds itself. In an acidic solution where the H$_3$O$^+$ ion concentration is high the equilibrium shifts to the left and the HIn colour predominates. In a solution which is alkaline the H$_3$O$^+$ ion concentration is low and the In$^-$ colour predominates.

Indicators change colour over a range of pH values. The pH range over which an indicator changes colour is determined by the strength of the acid (or base). Typically the range is given roughly by p$K_a \pm 1$.

### TEST YOURSELF

**15 Choose a suitable indicator to determine the end-point for each of the titrations illustrated in Figure 20.02.**

**16 Explain, in terms of Le Chatelier's principle, why an indicator shows its HIn colour when the pH is low but its In$^-$ colour when the pH is high.**

**17 The HIn colour is distinct so long as HIn > 10 × In$^-$ and the In$^-$ colour is distinct so long as In$^-$ > 10 × HIn. Use the logarithmic form of the equilibrium law (see page 109) to show that this means that the indicator will change colour over the range pH = p$K_a \pm 1$.**

| Indicator | p$K_a$ | colour change HIn/In$^-$ | pH range over which colour change occurs |
|-----------|--------|--------------------------|------------------------------------------|
| methyl orange | 3.6 | red/yellow | 3.2–4.2 |
| methyl red | 5.0 | yellow/red | 4.2–6.3 |
| bromothymol blue | 7.1 | yellow/blue | 6.0–7.6 |
| phenolphthalein | 9.4 | colourless/red | 8.2–10.0 |

20.03

# Buffer solutions

A buffer solution is a mixture of molecules and ions in solution that help to keep the pH more or less constant.

> **i** *A buffer solution cannot prevent pH changes but it evens out the large swings in pH that can occur without a buffer.*

Buffers are equilibrium systems that illustrate the practical importance of Le Chatelier's principle (see Chapter 11). A typical buffer mixture consists of a solution of a weak acid and one of its salts, for example a mixture of ethanoic acid and sodium ethanoate. There must be plenty of the acid and its salt.

$$CH_3CO_2H + H_2O \rightleftharpoons H_3O^+ + CH_3CO_2^-$$

acid molecules – a reservoir of H$^+$ ions

stays roughly constant – so the pH hardly changes

base ions – with the capacity to accept H$^+$ ions

Plenty of the weak acid to supply more H$^+$ ions if alkali is added

Plenty of ions from the salt to combine with extra H$^+$ ions if acid is added

20.04 **The action of a buffer solution. Enough of the buffering chemicals must be present to make sure that the buffer mixture determines the pH of the solution. There must be a large enough reservoir of both the un-ionised acid and of its salt**

By choosing the right weak acid, it is possible to prepare buffers at any pH value throughout the pH scale. If the concentrations of the weak acid and its salt are the same, then the pH of the buffer is equal to p$K_a$ for the acid.

More generally, the pH of a buffer mixture can be calculated with the logarithmic form of the equilibrium law (see page 109).

$$pH = pK_a + \log \frac{[salt]}{[acid]}$$

Diluting a buffer solution with water does not change the ratio of the concentrations of the salt and acid so the pH does not change (unless the dilution is so great that the assumptions made when deriving the equation no longer apply).

## WORKED EXAMPLE

What is the pH of a buffer solution containing 0.50 mol dm$^{-3}$ ethanoic acid and 1.00 mol dm$^{-3}$ sodium ethanoate?

### Notes on the answer

Look up the value of p$K_a$ in a book of data. The p$K_a$ of ethanoic acid is 4.8.

Use the equation: $pH = pK_a + \log \dfrac{[salt]}{[acid]}$

### Answer

$$pH = 4.8 + \log \frac{1.00}{0.50}$$
$$pH = 5.10$$

## Periodicity in the properties of chlorides

The chlorides of reactive metals are ionic. They dissolve in water to give neutral solutions. The chlorides of non-metals consist of covalent molecules and are normally hydrolysed by water.

|  | Polar covalent | | | | | |
|---|---|---|---|---|---|---|
| Ionic crystals | giant structures | | Covalent molecular gases and solids | | | |
| LiCl(s) | BeCl$_2$(s) | BCl$_3$(s) | CCl$_4$(l) | NCl$_3$(l) | Cl$_2$O(g) | ClF(g) |
| NaCl(s) | MgCl$_2$(s) | AlCl$_3$(s) | SiCl$_4$(l) | PCl$_5$(s) | S$_2$Cl$_2$(l) | Cl$_2$(g) |
|  |  |  | | PCl$_3$(l) | | |
| Dissolve in water giving a neutral solution | Partially hydrolysed to give an acidic solution | | Hydrolysed by water giving an acidic solution (unless inert as is CCl$_4$) | | | |

24.03 Formulae, structures, bonding and behaviour in water of chlorides in period 3

ℹ️ *Remember, hydrolysis is a reaction in which a compound is split apart in a reaction involving water.*

Hydrolysis of non-metal chlorides splits the compounds into an oxoacid or hydrated oxide of the non-metal and hydrogen halide. Non-metal chlorides

are typically molecular liquids at room temperature. Examples are $SiCl_4$ and $PCl_3$. Most of these compounds do not mix with water but react with it.

$$SiCl_4(l) + 2H_2O(l) \rightarrow SiO_2(s) + 4HCl(g)$$

## Group 4

The elements in Group 4 show a trend from non-metals at the top to metals at the bottom. All the elements have four electrons in their outer shell. The characteristic oxidation states of the group are $+4$ and $+2$. The $+2$ state becomes more important down the group and is the more stable state of lead.

### Definition

The **inert-pair effect** describes the observation that, for Groups 3, 4 and 5 of the periodic table, the oxidation state that is two below the highest state becomes increasingly stable down the group.

What this means is that two of the four electrons in the outer shell become less available for bonding down the group. The 'inert-pair effect' is best regarded as a reminder of a trend rather than an explanation.

### The elements

The two common allotropes of carbon (diamond and graphite) consist of covalent giant structures. Silicon and germanium have diamond-like giant structures. They are semi-conductors.

The room temperature allotrope of tin has a metallic structure. The low temperature allotrope, grey tin, has the non-metallic diamond structure. Lead has a metallic structure.

The two metals, tin and lead, have lower melting points than the non-metals with giant structures.

### The compounds

The Group 4 compounds in the +4 state generally behave more like the compounds of non-metals.

- The +4 oxides ($CO_2$, $SiO_2$, $SnO_2$ and $PbO_2$) are acidic or, in the case of tin and lead, amphoteric with a bias towards acidic oxide behaviour.

- The +4 chlorides are molecular liquids that (with the exception of $CCl_4$) are rapidly hydrolysed by water.

>  $CCl_4$ *does not react with water. This is an example of kinetic stability (inertness). The four large chlorine atoms prevent water molecules from using their lone pairs of electrons to attack the small central carbon atom.*

The compounds of tin and lead in the +2 state are more typical of metallic compounds.

- The +2 oxides (SnO and PbO) are amphoteric but with a bias towards basic oxide properties.

- The +2 chlorides are white solids. $PbCl_2$ is an ionic solid.

The +4 state is more stable for tin, so that tin(II) compounds are reducing agents. Tin(II) chloride reduces iron(III) to iron(II) for example.

The +2 state is the more stable state for lead. So $PbO_2$ is a strong oxidising agent. Lead(IV) oxide will oxidise chloride ions to chlorine gas.

**REVIEW**

Review the ideas about the periodicity of atomic and physical properties of the elements in Chapter 6.

Create a Mind Map to summarise the ideas about the periodicity of atomic, physical and chemical properties based on this chapter and Chapter 6.

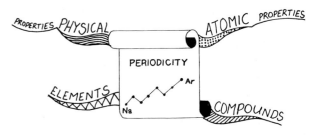

**24.04 Starting point for a Mind Map**

**TEST YOURSELF**

8 Write equations to illustrate:
   a  the acidic behaviour of carbon dioxide
   b  the amphoteric behaviour of SnO.

9 Use a table of standard electrode potentials to show that lead(IV) oxide can oxidise chloride ions to chlorine and write an equation for the overall reaction.

10 Draw and label a diagram to show the bonding and shape of a $CCl_4$ molecule.

11 List the similarities and differences between $CCl_4$ and $SiCl_4$. Account for the differences in terms of structure and bonding.

12 Write an equation for the reduction of iron(III) ions by tin(II) ions.

## Addition polymers

Molecules of compounds with C=C bonds can join together in long chains to form polymers (see Section 13.5).

## Structures of addition polymers

The properties of some addition polymers depend on the way in which the side chains are arranged.

In isotactic poly(propene), for example, all the methyl side chains are on the same side of the carbon chain. The molecules coil into a regular helical shape and pack together to form a highly crystalline polymer, which is very strong. This is the form of the polymer that is useful for hard-wearing fibres, tough mouldings in motor vehicles and containers that can hold boiling water.

There is another form of poly(propene) in which the side groups along the polymer chain are randomly

## Polymers

Polymers are long chain molecules. Natural polymers include proteins, polysaccharides (see carbohydrates) and nucleic acids. Synthetic polymers include polyesters, polyamides and the many polymers formed by the addition polymerisation of compounds with C=C bonds.

> **i** *The properties of polymers are very varied. Polymeric materials include plastics, elastomers and fibres.*

**31.01 Structure of isotactic poly(propene) with all the methyl groups on the same side of the carbon chain**

orientated. This is atactic poly(propene), which is an amorphous, rubbery polymer of little value, unlike isotactic poly(propene).

**31.02 Part of a chain of atactic poly(propene)**

> ### TEST YOURSELF
>
> 3 There is a third form of poly(propene) which, like the isotactic form, has a regular arrangement of the methyl groups. Draw a short length of this syndiotactic form in which the methyl groups alternate from one side of the chain to the other.

## Mechanism of addition polymerisation

One method for initiating the polymerisation of a compound with a C=C bond is to use a peroxide.

> ### Factfile
>
> **Peroxides**
>
> Peroxides are compounds related to hydrogen peroxide, $H_2O_2$. Organic peroxides can act as a source of free radicals to initiate addition polymerisation of unsaturated compounds.
>
> **31.03 A benzoyl peroxide molecule splitting to form two free radicals. The O—O bond is relatively weak**

Free-radical polymerisation takes place in three stages just like other free-radical chain reactions (see Section 13.2).

**Initiation** – the step that produces free radicals.

$$R—O—O—R \longrightarrow 2\,R—O^{\bullet}$$

**Propagation** – steps that produce products and more free radicals.

$$RO^{\bullet}\ H_2C=CH_2 \longrightarrow R—O—CH_2—CH_2^{\bullet}$$

$$R—O—CH_2—CH_2^{\bullet}\ H_2C=CH_2 \longrightarrow R—O—(CH_2)_3—CH_2^{\bullet}$$

**Termination** – steps that remove free radicals by turning them into molecules.

$$2\,R—O—(CH_2)_n—CH_2^{\bullet} \longrightarrow$$
$$R—O—(CH_2)_n—CH_2—CH_2—(CH_2)_n—O—R$$

> ### TEST YOURSELF
>
> 4 Use the formation of free radicals from organic peroxides to explain the term homolytic fission.

## Condensation polymers

Condensation polymers are produced by a series of condensation reactions splitting off a small molecule, such as water, between the functional groups of the monomers. Examples of condensation polymers are polyamides and polyesters. Where each monomer has two functional groups, this type of polymerisation produces chains.

> ℹ *Cross linking is possible if one of the monomers has three functional groups.*

> ### Definitions
>
> A **condensation reaction** is a reaction in which molecules join together by splitting off a small molecule such as water. The formation of an ester from an acid and an alcohol is a condensation reaction.
>
> **Cross linking** is the formation of chemical bonds between polymer chains to modify the properties of polymers.

## Polyamides

Polyamides are polymers in which the monomer molecules are linked by amide bonds. The first important polyamides were formed by condensation polymerisation between diamines and dicarboxylic acids.

Polymeric aryl amides are called aramids. An example of an aramid is Kevlar. The rigid, linear polymer chains in Kevlar line up parallel to each other, held together by hydrogen bonding.

## Polyesters

Polyesters are polymers formed by condensation polymerisation between acids with two carboxylic acid groups and alcohols with two or more —OH groups. The units in the polymer chains are linked by a series of ester bonds.

**31.04  Condensation polymerisation to make nylon-6,6. The numbers in the name indicate the numbers of carbon atoms in the two monomers**

**31.05  The monomers for making polyester fibres are benzene-1,4-dicarboxylic acid and ethan-1,2-diol**

*i The traditional name for these compounds are terephthalic acid and ethylene glycol. Hence the commercial name Terylene for one brand of polyester.*

*i The alternative name for the polymer is polyethylene terephthalate, which gives rise to the name PET when the same polymer is used as a plastic to make bottles for carbonated drinks.*

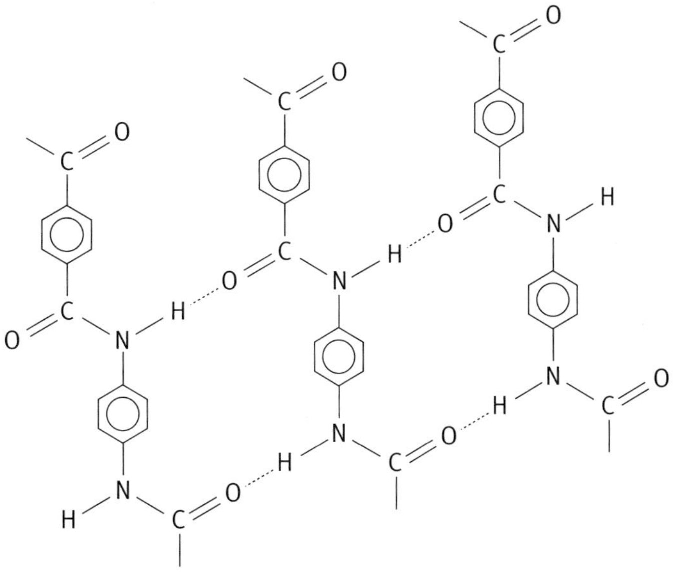

**31.06 The structure of Kevlar**

**T E S T   Y O U R S E L F**

5 **Show that Kevlar is a polymer of benzene-1,4-diamine and benzene-1,4-dicarboxylic acid.**

6 **Show that polypeptides are condensation polymers (see Section 30.4).**

7 **Draw the structure of the condensation polymer made from:**

   **a**

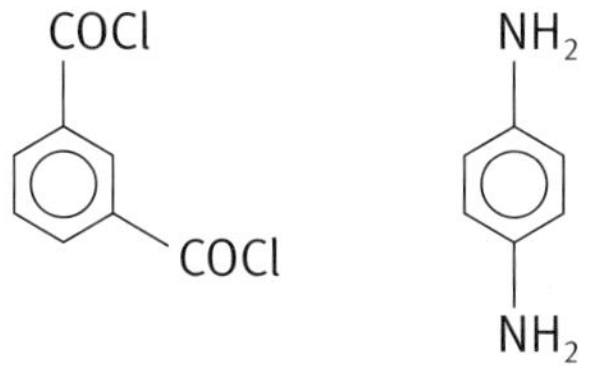

   **b  2-hydroxypropanoic acid.**

## Polymer properties and uses

Plastics are materials made of long-chain molecules, which at some stage can be easily moulded into shape. Thermoplastics become plastic materials when they are hot and harden on cooling. Some thermoplastics are rigid and brittle at room temperature such as polystyrene. Other thermoplastics are flexible such as polythene.

*Once moulded, a plastic material keeps its new shape; unlike an elastomer, which tends to spring back to its original shape.*

**D e f i n i t i o n**

**Biodegradable materials** break down in the environment due to the action of micro-organisms.

**T E S T   Y O U R S E L F**

8 **a Suggest environmental benefits of biodegradable polymers.**
   **b Which types of synthetic polymer are more likely to be biodegradable: addition polymers or condensation polymers? Why?**

9 **Polyesters and polyamides are suitable as fibres for clothing. Polymers that make good fibres generally have strong intermolecular forces between the chains. Identify the features of a nylon molecule that give rise to strong inter-chain forces.**

**R E V I E W**

**Draw a Mind Map to summarise important aspects of polymer chemistry. See also Sections 13.5 and 30.4.**

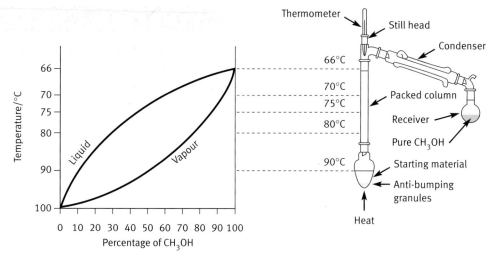

**32.03** Boiling-point composition diagram for a mixture of methanol and water. Methanol boils at a lower temperature so it is the more volatile substance. Boiling any mixture of the liquids produces a vapour that is richer in methanol

**T E S T   Y O U R S E L F**

4   Indicate the sequence of techniques you would use in the laboratory to make and identify:
    a   1-bromobutane from butan-1-ol
    b   propanoic acid from propan-1-ol
    c   2-ethanoylhydroxybenzoic acid (aspirin) from 2-hydroxybenzoic acid and ethanoic anhydride.

5   a   Use Figure 32.03 to estimate the composition of the vapour formed at first on heating a mixture of 10% methanol and 90% water.
    b   Estimate the composition of the liquid if this vapour condenses and evaporates again and condenses once more.

## Tests for functional groups

In a modern laboratory, organic analysis is based on a range of automated and instrumental techniques, including combustion analysis, mass spectrometry, IR spectroscopy, UV spectroscopy and nuclear magnetic resonance spectroscopy (see Chapter 33).

**i** *Melting points and boiling points provide a check on the identity and purity of compounds.*

Traditionally, chemical tests helped to identify functional groups in organic molecules. Examples are shown in Figure 32.04. Other tests include the tri-iodomethane reaction (see Section 28.3) and the use of potassium dichromate(VI) to distinguish primary, secondary and tertiary alcohols (see Section 15.2).

**T E S T   Y O U R S E L F**

6   For each pair of compounds, suggest chemical tests for distinguishing between them. State the result of the tests for both compounds in each pair.
    a   cyclohexene and cyclohexanol
    b   1-bromobutane and 1-iodobutane
    c   butan-2-ol and 2-methylpropan-2-ol
    d   butan-1-ol and butanal
    e   butan-1-ol and butanoic acid.

| Functional group | Test | Observations |
|---|---|---|
| >C=C< in an alkene | • Shake with a dilute solution of bromine<br>• Shake with a very dilute, acidic solution of potassium manganate(VII) | • Orange colour of the solution decolourised<br>• Purple colour fades and the solution turns colourless |
| —C—X where X = Cl, Br or I in a halogenoalkane | • Warm with a solution of sodium hydroxide. Cool. Acidify with nitric acid. Then add silver nitrate solution | • Precipitate is white from a chloro compound, creamy yellow from a bromo compound and yellow from an iodo compound. (Hydrolysis produces ions from the covalent molecules) |
| —C—OH in a primary alcohol | • Add a solution of sodium hydrogencarbonate<br>• Add PCl₅ to the **anhydrous** compound<br>• Warm with an acidic solution of potassium dichromate(VI) | • No reaction. Unlike acids, alcohols do not react with carbonates<br>• Colourless, fuming gas forms (hydrogen chloride)<br>• Orange solution turns green and gives a fruity smelling vapour. Alcohols are oxidised by dichromate(VI) but not by Fehling's solution |
| >C=O in aldehydes and ketones | • Add 2,4-dinitrophenylhydrazine solution<br>• Warm with fresh Fehling's solution<br>• Warm with fresh Tollens' reagent | • Aldehydes and ketones both give yellow or red precipitates<br>• Solution turns greenish and then an orange-red precipitate forms with aldehydes, but not ketones<br>• Silver mirror forms with aldehydes but not with ketones |
| —CO₂H in carboxylic acids | • Measure the pH of a solution<br>• Add a solution of sodium hydrogencarbonate<br>• Add a neutral solution of iron(III) chloride | • Acidic solution with pH about 3–4<br>• Mixture fizzes giving off carbon dioxide<br>• Methanoic and ethanoic acids give a red colouration |

**32.04  Chemical tests used to identify functional groups in organic molecules**

## REVIEW

**Devise a Mind Map to summarise the relationships between all the main functional groups and series of organic compounds that you have studied.**

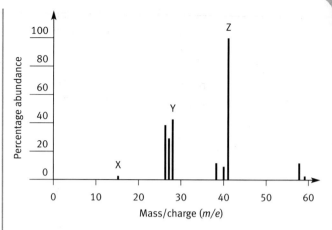

**33.01   Mass spectrum of butane, $C_4H_{10}$, showing the parent ion with a value 58**

## PREVIEW

**By the end of this topic you will be able to:**

✔ interpret fragmentation patterns from a mass spectrometer

✔ interpret infra-red spectra

✔ interpret ultraviolet/visible spectra

✔ interpret nuclear magnetic resonance spectra.

## Mass spectrometer

### Molecular masses and structures

Section 1.2 describes the use of a mass spectrometer to measure relative atomic masses and isotopic abundances.

When analysing molecular compounds, the molecules are bombarded by high energy electrons, turning them into ions.

$$M + e^- \rightarrow M^+ + 2e^-$$

high energy        low energy

## Definitions

A **molecular ion** forms when a molecule loses an electron when bombarded by a high energy electron. This ion has an unpaired electron so it is often represented as $M^+$.

The **mass to charge ratio** ($m/z$) is the ratio of the relative mass of the ion to its charge where $z$ is the number of charges (1, 2 and so on).

Molecular ions are unstable and break up into fragments. The fragments are a mixture of ions and free radicals.

> ℹ️ *The uncharged radicals do not show up in the mass spectrum, which takes the form of a 'fragmentation pattern'.*

When analysing molecular compounds, the peak of the ion with the highest mass to charge ratio is usually the whole molecule ionised by losing just one electron. So the mass of this 'parent ion' is the relative molecular mass of the compound.

The fragments that show up in the spectrum are all positive ions. The highest peaks generally correspond to positive ions that are relatively more stable, such as tertiary carbocations or ions stabilised by delocalisation, such as $RCO^+$ (the acylium ion).

Chemists who synthesise new compounds can study their fragmentation patterns. They identify the fragments from their masses and then piece together likely structures with the help of evidence from other methods of analysis, such as infra-red spectroscopy and nuclear magnetic resonance spectroscopy.

## TEST YOURSELF

1   Suggest the identity of the fragments X, Y and Z in the mass spectrum of butane in Figure 33.01.

2   What, according to Figure 33.01, is the relative molecular mass of butane?

3   The mass spectrum of 2,2,5-trimethylpentane has a very strong peak with a mass to charge ratio of 57. Suggest the structure of the ion that gives rise to this peak and explain why it gives a strong signal.

4   Use symbols to show how the molecular ion of pentane splits into ions and free radicals to give peaks with mass to charge ratios of 15, 29, 43 and 57.

## Infra-red spectra

Infra-red (IR) spectroscopy is an analytical technique used to identify functional groups in organic molecules. Most compounds absorb IR radiation.

The wavelengths they absorb correspond to the natural frequencies at which vibrating bonds in the molecules bend and stretch.

> **i** *It is polar bonds such as O—H, C—O and C=O, that absorb strongly as they vibrate.*

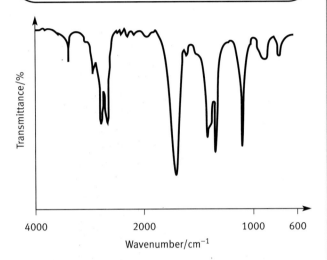

**33.02  IR spectra of ethanal. The units along the bottom are wavenumbers (in cm⁻¹). IR wavenumbers range from 400 cm⁻¹ to 4500 cm⁻¹**

## Definition

The **wavenumber** is the number of waves in 1 cm. Transmittance on the vertical axis measures the percentage of radiation that passes through the sample. The troughs appear at the wavenumbers that the compound absorbs strongly.

Bonds vibrate in particular ways and absorb radiation at specific wavelengths. This means that it is possible to look at an IR spectrum, especially in the range of wavenumbers from 1000 cm⁻¹ to 4000 cm⁻¹, and identify particular functional groups.

### Factfile

**IR absorption range**

| Bond | Range of wavenumbers/cm⁻¹ |
| --- | --- |
| C—H | 2850–3300 |
| C=C | 1620–1680 |
| C=O | 1680–1750 |
| C—O | 1000–1300 |
| O—H (alcohols) | 3230–3550 |
| O—H (acids) | 2500–3000 |

> **i** *Hydrogen bonding broadens the —OH peaks in the spectra of alcohols and carboxylic acids.*

Molecules with several atoms can vibrate in many ways because the vibrations of one bond affect others close to it. The complex pattern of vibrations (in the region 650 cm⁻¹ to 1500 cm⁻¹) can be used as a 'fingerprint' to be matched against the recorded IR spectrum in a database.

> **i** *Comparing the IR spectrum of a product of synthesis with the spectrum of the pure compound can be used to check that the product is pure.*

### TEST YOURSELF

5  A compound, Q, with the molecular formula $C_4H_{10}O$ has a broad peak in its IR spectrum at 3500 cm⁻¹. Oxidation of Q with excess potassium dichromate(VI) gives a product, R, which does not reduce Fehling's solution. R has a strong peak in its IR spectrum at 1700 cm⁻¹. Identify Q and R.

## Ultraviolet and visible spectra

Ultraviolet (UV) spectroscopy is particularly useful for studying colourless organic molecules with unsaturated functional groups such as C=C and C=O. The molecules absorb UV radiation at frequencies which excite shared electrons in double bonds. A UV spectrometer records the extent to which samples absorb UV radiation across a range of wavelengths.

In organic molecules with conjugated systems, the UV absorption peak moves to longer wavelengths as the number of alternating double and single bonds increases. The maximum absorption by ethene is at

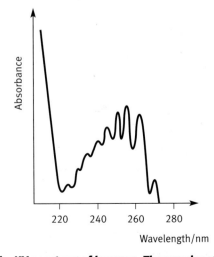

**33.03  The UV spectrum of benzene. The wavelength at which maximum absorption occurs, λₘₐₓ, is characteristic of the compound**

185 nm; this shifts to 220 nm for buta-1,3-diene. These are both colourless compounds.

### Definition

A **conjugated system** is a system of alternate double and single bonds in a molecule. Organic molecules with extended conjugated systems absorb radiation in the visible part of the spectrum and are therefore coloured.

The longer the conjugated chain of alternating double and single bonds, the stronger the absorption. Beta-carotene, with eleven conjugated carbon-carbon

### TEST YOURSELF

**6 a These two structures show phenolphthalein in acid and in alkali.**

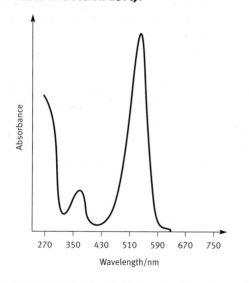

**Account for the fact that phenolphthalein is colourless in acid and purply-red in alkali.**

**b Which form of the indicator has the absorption spectrum shown below (see table in Section 25.4)?**

double bonds, absorbs strongly with a peak shifted so far that it is not in the UV region. It lies in the blue region of the visible spectrum (450 nm), so carotene is bright orange.

## Nuclear magnetic resonance spectra

Nuclear magnetic resonance (nmr) spectroscopy is a powerful analytical technique for finding the structures of carbon compounds. The technique is used to identify unknown compounds, to check for impurities and to study the shapes of molecules.

The name of the technique summarises the key features:

- **nuclear** – the technique detects nuclei of atoms such as hydrogen-1 (protons)

- **magnetic** – the nuclei detected by the technique are the ones that act like tiny magnets that can line up either in the same direction or in the opposite direction to an external magnetic field

- **resonance** – the absorption of energy from radiowaves, with the frequency corresponding to the size of the energy jump as the nuclei flip from one alignment in a magnetic field to the other.

The sample is dissolved in a solvent with no hydrogen-1 atoms. Also in the solution is some tetramethyl silane (TMS), which is a standard reference compound that produces an absorption peak well away from the peaks from samples.

The recorder prints out a spectrum with peaks wherever the sample absorbs radiation strongly. The zero on the scale is fixed by the absorption of hydrogen atoms in the reference chemical TMS.

### Definition

The distances of the sample peaks from zero defined by TMS are called their **chemical shifts** ($\delta$).

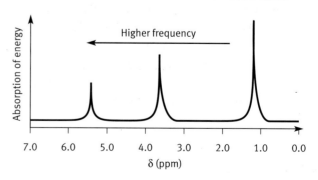

**33.04 nmr spectrum for ethanol at low resolution. The integration trace gives a measure of the area under each peak**

Study and Revise AS and A2 Level Chemistry

Each peak corresponds to hydrogen nuclei in different chemical situations. The area under a peak is proportional to the number of nuclei in each situation. In ethanol, $CH_3CH_2OH$, there are hydrogen nuclei in three environments, which have different chemical shifts.

| Type of proton | Chemical shift/ppm |
|---|---|
| $R-CH_3$ | 0.9 |
| $R-CH_2-R$ | 1.3 |
| $R_3CH$ | 2.0 |
| $R-CO-CH_3$ | 2.1 |
| $R-CH_2-CO-R$ | 2.5 |
| $R-CHO$ | 9.7 |

At high resolution it is possible to produce nmr spectra with more detail, which provide even more information about molecular structures.

*i* *Protons connected to neighbouring atoms interact with each other. Chemists call this interaction 'coupling' and they find that the effect is to split the peaks into a number of lines.*

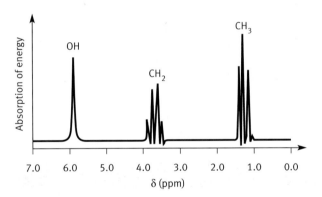

**33.05 High resolution nmr spectrum for ethanol**

Hydrogen atoms in —OH and —$NH_2$ groups rapidly exchange protons with each other. These 'labile' protons do not interact with neighbouring protons and so show up as single peaks in nmr spectra.

Note the extra peaks compared with the low resolution spectrum. This illustrates the 'n + 1' rule. A peak from protons bonded to an atom that is next to

an atom with two protons splits into three lines. A peak from protons bonded to an atom that is next to an atom with three protons splits into four lines.

*i* *It is the number of hydrogen atoms of a particular type that determines the area under each peak.*

*i* *It is the number of hydrogen atoms on an adjacent carbon atom that decides whether the peak is a singlet, doublet or triplet.*

**TEST YOURSELF**

7   This is the low resolution nmr spectrum of a compound $C_4H_8O$.

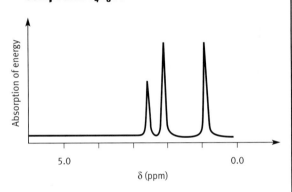

a   **Suggest a displayed formula for the compound.**

b   **Account for the relative heights of the three peaks.**

c   **How would you expect the three peaks to appear in the high resolution spectrum of this compound?**

**REVIEW**

**Develop a Mind Map of instrumental methods of analysis.**

## Chapter 1

1. a 1p, 1n, 1e
   b 2p 2n, 2e
   c 8p, 8n, 8e
   d 35p, 44n, 36e
   e 12p, 12n, 10e
2. a $^{3}_{1}H$
   b $^{31}_{15}P$
   c $^{7}_{3}Li^+$
   d $^{14}_{7}N^{3-}$
3. 20.18
4. 24.33
5. Number of orbitals per shell $= n^2$
   Max 2 electrons per shell.
6. a Hydrogen
   b Nitrogen
   c Calcium
7. a $1s^2 2s^2 2p^1$
   b $1s^2 2s^2 2p^5$
   c $1s^2 2s^2 2p^6 3s^2$
   d $1s^2 2s^2 2p^6 3s^2 3p^5$
8. 3, Group 3
9. Sketch graph (similar to Figure 01.08) to show 2e removed relatively easily, then 8e and then 2e.

## Chapter 2

1. a $1.51 \times 10^{23}$
   b $24.1 \times 10^{23}$
   c $18.1 \times 10^{23}$
   d $12.0 \times 10^{23}$
2. a 0.25 mol
   b 0.25 mol
   c 0.25 mol
3. a 381 g
   b 31.5 g
   c 0.28 g
4. a $CuFeS_2$
   b $SiO_2$
   c $Na_2SO_4$
   d $C_2H_6O$
5. water: $H_2O$, 18
   ethane: $C_2H_6$
   benzene: CH, 78
   hydrazine: $N_2H_4$
6. a $Ca(s) + 2H_2O(l) \rightarrow Ca(OH)_2(s) + H_2(g)$
   b $Ca(OH)_2(s) + 2HCl(aq) \rightarrow CaCl_2(aq) + 2H_2O(l)$
   c $Fe_2O_3(s) + 2Al(s) \rightarrow 2Fe(s) + Al_2O_3(s)$
   d $4NH_3(g) + 5O_2(g) \rightarrow 4NO(g) + 6H_2O(g)$
7. a 3.2 g
   b 8.52 g
   c 460 g
8. 5.2 g
9. a 11.3 g
   b 60.2%
10. 100 cm$^3$, 60 cm$^3$
11. HCl(g), 20 cm$^3$
12. $3 \times 10^6$ cm$^3$
13. 12.5 g
14. a 0.1 mol dm$^{-3}$
    b 0.05 mol dm$^{-3}$
    c 0.4 mol dm$^{-3}$
15. a 0.0125 mol
    b 0.2 mol
    c 0.002 mol
16. 1.16 g
17. 600 cm$^3$
18. 25 cm$^3$
19. 2 mol dm$^{-3}$
20. n = 2

## Chapter 3

1. a $A \rightarrow B$: solid heating up
   $B \rightarrow C$: solid melting
   $C \rightarrow D$: liquid heating up
   $D \rightarrow E$: liquid evaporating
2. Impure solids do not melt at a sharp temperature, so line $B \rightarrow C$ would slope upwards.
3. 58.4 g mol$^{-1}$
4. Molecular: water, bromine, sulfuric acid.
   Giant: graphite, silicon dioxide, iron, sodium chloride.
5. a Aluminium coating on a telescope mirror.
   b Copper electricity cables.
   c Steel plate pressed into shape for parts of car bodies.
6. a All 1+
   b All 2+
   c 3+
   d 3−
   e Both 2−
   f All 1−
7. a $NH_4Cl$
   b $Na_2O$
   c $K_2CO_3$
   d $Ca(NO_3)_2$
   e $Al_2(SO_4)_3$
8. a Na$^\times$ · $\ddot{\underset{..}{F}}$ : give Na$^+$ : $\ddot{\underset{..}{F}}$ :$^-$

   b Mg$^\times$ $\ddot{\underset{..}{O}}$ : give Mg$^{2+}$ $^\times_\times\ddot{\underset{..}{O}}$ :$^{2-}$

   c Na$^\times$ Na$^\times$ $\ddot{\underset{..}{S}}$ : give Na$^+$ Na$^+$ $^\times\ddot{\underset{..}{S}}^\times$ :$^{2-}$
9. a It is ionic. The charged ions must be free to move to carry a current.
   b At the cathode: $Al^{3+} + 3e^- \rightarrow Al$
   At the anode: $2O^{2-} \rightarrow O_2 + 4e^-$
   c The process is used to manufacture aluminium. Aluminium oxide melts at a very high temperature. Mixed with calcium aluminium fluoride, its melting point is much lower and this makes the process of electrolysis feasible.
10. a : $\ddot{\underset{..}{Br}}$ $^{\times\times}_{\times\times}\ddot{Br}$ :

    b H $\overset{\times\times}{\underset{\times\times}{Cl}}$ :

    c H $\overset{\times\times}{\underset{\times\times}{S}}$ H

    d $^\times_\times\overset{}{\underset{}{S}}$ : C : $^\times_\times S^\times$
11. a

$$H - \underset{\underset{H}{|}}{\overset{\overset{H}{|}}{N}} \overset{+}{\rightarrow} H$$

**11 b**

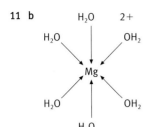

**12**

**13**

polar   polar   polar

non-polar   polar   polar

14 HI: permanent dipole–permanent dipole
C₄H₁₀: temporary dipole–temporary dipole
C₂H₅OH: hydrogen bonding

15 Hydrogen bonding between methanol molecules is much stronger than the temporary dipole–temporary dipole attractions between non-polar propane molecules.

**16 a**

**b**

17 Polarisability increases from HF to HI as the number of full shells increases from one halogen atom to the next. Fluorine is so electronegative that HF is affected by hydrogen bonding, which is stronger than the intermolecular forces between the other hydrogen halides.

18 The longer a molecule and the more electrons, the greater the surface area over which intermolecular forces can attract it to neighbouring molecules. An ethene molecule has just two atoms, while poly(ethene) consists of molecules with many thousands of atoms.

19 The branched hydrocarbon is more compact with a smaller surface area over which intermolecular forces can act than the unbranched hydrocarbon.

20 $CO_2$ consists of small molecules held together by weak intermolecular forces. The atoms in silicon dioxide make-up a giant structure held together by strong covalent bonds.

21 Molecular: $N_2$, $S_8$, $Cl_2$, $Br_2$
Giant: C, Si

22 Covalent: methane, fluorine
Polar covalent: silicon tetrachloride
Ionic with some covalent character: magnesium chloride, aluminium chloride, magnesium sulfide
Ionic: sodium chloride, lithium fluoride

## Chapter 4

1 $\Delta H^{\ominus}_{c} = -1940 \text{ kJ mol}^{-1}$
2 $\Delta H = -11 \text{ kJ mol}^{-1}$
3 $\Delta H = -54.6 \text{ kJ mol}^{-1}$ (per mole of NaOH)
4 $C_4H_{10}(g) + 6^1/_2O_2(g) \rightarrow 4CO_2(g) + 5H_2O(l)$
5 $2C(s) + 3H_2(g) + {}^1/_2O_2(g) \rightarrow C_2H_5OH(l)$
6 $H_2(g) + {}^1/_2O_2(g) \rightarrow H_2O(l)$
7 $\Delta H^{\ominus}_{f} = -75 \text{ kJ mol}^{-1}$
8 There is an enthalpy change when water evaporates or steam condenses.
9 $\Delta H^{\ominus}_{reaction} = -136.9 \text{ kJ mol}^{-1}$
10 $\Delta H = -415 \text{ kJ mol}^{-1}$
11 Enthalpies of formation are specific for the compounds involved and so give the more accurate value.

## Chapter 5

1 a $Mg \rightarrow Mg^{2+} + 2e^-$
   $Cl_2 + 2e^- \rightarrow 2Cl^-$
  b $Cu \rightarrow Cu^{2+} + 2e^-$
   ${}^1/_2O_2 + 2e^- \rightarrow O^{2-}$
  c $2Li \rightarrow 2Li^+ + 2e^-$
   $\underline{I_2 + 2e^- \rightarrow 2I^-}$
2 a $Zn \rightarrow Zn^{2+} + 2e^-$
   $\underline{Cu^{2+} + 2e^- \rightarrow Cu}$
   $Zn + Cu^{2+} \rightarrow Zn^{2+} + Cu$
  b $2Br^- \rightarrow Br_2 + 2e^-$
   $\underline{Cl_2 + 2e^- \rightarrow 2Cl^-}$
   $Cl_2 + 2Br^- \rightarrow 2Cl^- + Br_2$
  c $2Fe^{2+} \rightarrow 2Fe^{3+} + 2e^-$
   $Cl_2 + 2e^- \rightarrow 2Cl^-$
   $2Fe^{2+} + Cl_2 \rightarrow 2Fe^{3+} + 2Cl^-$
3 a +3
  b +7
  c +4
  d +3
  e −2
4 a Ni oxidised
  b Br reduced
  c I oxidised
  d O reduced
  e Na oxidised
5 a manganese(IV) oxide
  b chromium(III) oxide
  c sodium chlorate(I)
  d potassium iodate(V)
  e phosphorus(V) acid
6 a $2NH_3(g) + 2^1/_2O_2(g) \rightarrow 2NO(g) + 3H_2O(g)$
  b $2S_2O_3^{2-}(aq) + I_2(aq) \rightarrow S_4O_6^{2-}(aq) + 2I^-(aq)$
  c $2I^-(aq) + H_2O_2(l) + 2H^+(aq) \rightarrow I_2(aq) + 2H_2O(l)$
  d $Cu(s) + 4HNO_3(aq) \rightarrow Cu(NO_3)_2(aq) + 2NO_2(g) + 2H_2O(l)$

## Chapter 6

1 s-block: Be – $1s^2 2s^2$
  p-block: N – $1s^2 2s^2 2p^3$
  s-block: K – $1s^2 2s^2 2p^6 3s^2 3p^6 4s^1$
  d-block: Ti – $1s^2 2s^2 2p^6 3s^2 3p^6 3d^2 4s^2$

**2** Similarities: they rise and then fall across each period; Group 4 elements are at or near the peaks

**3** Ar, Cl, S, P, Mg, Na

**4** Group 1: 1+
Group 2: 2+
Group 3: 3+
Group 6: 2−
Group 7: 1−

# Chapter 7

**1 a** $Mg(s) + 2HCl(aq) \rightarrow MgCl_2(aq) + H_2(g)$
**b** $MgO(s) + 2HCl(aq) \rightarrow MgCl_2(aq) + H_2O(l)$
**c** $MgCO_3(s) + 2HCl(aq) \rightarrow MgCl_2(aq) + CO_2(g) + H_2O(l)$

**2 a** $H^+$, $SO_4^{2-}$
**b** $NH_4^+$, $OH^-$

**3 a** potassium nitrate, $KNO_3$
**b** calcium chloride, $CaCl_2$
**c** magnesium sulfate, $MgSO_4$
**d** ammonium ethanoate, $CH_3CO_2NH_4$

**4 a** barium sulfate, $BaSO_4$
**b** silver bromide, $AgBr$

**5** Rb: $1s^2 2s^2 2p^6 3s^2 3p^6 3d^{10} 4s^2 4p^6 5s^1$

**6 a** A Li atom loses the one electron in the outer shell when turning into $Li^+$.
**b** A Li atom has one less full shell than an Na atom.
**c** Shielding means that the effective nuclear charge for outer electrons is 1+ in all Group 1 metal atoms. The outer electron in a Li atom is closer to the nucleus than the outer electron in Na, so it is held more strongly.

**7**

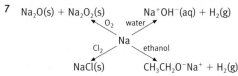

**8 a** $Li_2O(s) + H_2O(l) \rightarrow 2LiOH(aq)$
**b** $Na_2O(s) + 2HCl(aq) \rightarrow 2NaCl(aq) + H_2O(l)$

**9** Sr: $1s^2 2s^2 2p^6 3s^2 3p^6 3d^{10} 4s^2 4p^6 5s^2$

**10 a** A Mg atom loses the two electrons in the outer shell when turning into $Mg^{2+}$.
**b** A Mg atom has one fewer full shells than a Ca atom.
**c** Shielding means that the effective nuclear charge for outer electrons is 2+ in all Group 2 metal atoms. The outer electrons in a Mg atom is closer to the nucleus than the outer electrons in Ca, so they are held more strongly.

**11**

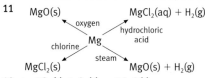

**12 a** $2Ca(s) + O_2(g) \rightarrow 2CaO(s)$
**b** $Mg(s) + H_2O(g) \rightarrow MgO(s) + H_2(g)$
**c** $Sr(s) + Cl_2(g) \rightarrow SrCl_2(s)$
**d** $CaO(s) + H_2O(l) \rightarrow Ca(OH)_2(s)$
**e** $BaCO_3(s) + 2HCl(aq) \rightarrow BaCl_2(aq) + CO_2(g) + H_2O(l)$

**13** $Ba^{2+}(aq) + SO_4^{2-}(aq) \rightarrow BaSO_4(s)$

**15** $MgCO_3(s) \rightarrow MgO(s) + CO_2(g)$
$CaCO_3(s) \rightarrow CaO(s) + CO_2(g)$
$MgCO_3$ decomposes at a lower temperature.

# Chapter 8

**1 a** $1s^2 2s^2 2p^6$
**b** $1s^2 2s^2 2p^6 3s^2 3p^6$

**2 a** $2Fe(s) + 3Br_2(l) \rightarrow 2FeBr_3(s)$
**b** $Cl_2(aq) + 2Br^-(aq) \rightarrow 2Cl^-(aq) + Br_2(aq)$

**3** $I_2 + 2e^- \rightarrow 2I^-$

**4** The solution turns yellow, then brown as iodine forms and dissolves in excess potassium iodide. On adding more bromine, grey crystals of iodine appear, because bromine is more reactive than iodine and it displaces the iodine to form potassium bromide.

**5** The intermolecular forces in HF are hydrogen bonds because fluorine is so electronegative. Hydrogen bonds are stronger than other intermolecular forces. None of the other hydrogen halides are affected by hydrogen bonding.

**6** A strong acid is fully ionised in solution:
$HBr(aq) \rightarrow H^+(aq) + Br^-(aq)$

**7 a** $H_2SO_4(l) + NaCl(s) \rightarrow HCl(g) + NaHSO_4(s)$
**b** $H_2SO_4(l) + KBr(s) \rightarrow HBr(g) + NaHSO_4(s)$, then
$2HBr(g) + H_2SO_4(l) \rightarrow 2H_2O(l) + SO_2(g) + Br_2(g)$

**8 a** An acid-base reaction
**b** An acid-base reaction followed by a redox reaction.

**9**

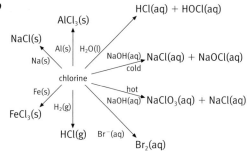

**10** $1.01$ mol dm$^{-3}$

**11 a** Oxidation at the anode: $2Cl^- \rightarrow Cl_2 + 2e^-$
Reduction at the cathode: $2H^+ + 2e^- \rightarrow H_2$
**b** $NaCl(aq)$ contains these ions. $Na^+$, $Cl^-$, $H^+$, $OH^-$. Discharge of $Cl^-$ and $H^+$ leaves $NaOH(aq)$.
**c and d** Chlorine reacts with sodium hydroxide making sodium chlorate(I) bleach

**12** Stages 1 and 4 chlorine oxidises bromide ions:
$Cl_2(aq) + 2Br^-(aq) \rightarrow 2Cl^-(aq) + Br_2(aq)$
Stage 3: Sulfur dioxide reduces bromine to bromide ions:
$Br_2(aq) + SO_2(aq) + 2H_2O(l)$
$\rightarrow 2Br^-(aq) + SO_4^{2-}(aq) + 4H^+(aq)$

# Chapter 9

**1 a** $2Fe_2O_3(s) + 3C(s) \rightarrow 4Fe(l) + 3CO_2(g)$
**b** $CaCO_3(s) \rightarrow CaO(s) + CO_2(g)$

**2 a** $Mg(s) + S \rightarrow MgS(s)$
**b** $Si + O_2(g) \rightarrow SiO_2(s)$
$SiO_2(s) + CaO(s) \rightarrow CaSiO_3(s)$
**c** $4Al(s) + 3O_2(g) \rightarrow 2Al_2O_3(s)$

**3** Aluminium oxide is amphoteric and will dissolve in concentrated alkali. This distinguishes it from iron(III) oxide, which is basic and does not react with alkali.

**4** The electrolysis process is only economical with cheap electricity.

**5** The oxygen formed at the graphite anodes during electrolysis reacts with the carbon, forming carbon dioxide. So the anodes burn away.

**6** The metal has a low density but forms strong alloys that resist corrosion and so retain their shiny appearance. The metal is also a good conductor of electricity.

**7** Argon keeps out oxygen, which would react with the metals in the reactor. Argon is a very unreactive noble gas.

8   Sodium reacts with water forming sodium hydroxide, which is very corrosive. It reacts with hydrochloric acid to form sodium chloride (salt), which can be safely removed in solution.

9   Metals are easier to identify and separate from other wastes. Metals are relatively high value and so the effort needed for recycling is worthwhile. After remelting, the metals are 'as good as new'.

10  Recycling helps to preserve scarce resources. Less energy is required to recycle metals than to produce metals from ores by mining, mineral processing and chemical reduction. Recycling has much less impact on the environment than extraction of metals from ores. Recycling means that there is less waste to be disposed of by other means.

# Chapter 10

1   Collect the hydrogen gas produced over water in a graduated vessel, such as a measuring cylinder. Measure the gas volume at regular intervals.

2
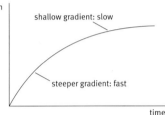

3   a   Alkali (NaOH or KOH)
    b   Vanadium(V) oxide
    c   Iron
    d   Platinum (maybe alloyed with rhodium)
    e   Zeolite
    f   Acid (such as sulfuric acid)

4
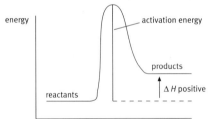

5   Bonds stretch or break as molecules collide and react. Bond breaking is endothermic. The activation energy for a reaction is the energy needed to stretch and break bonds during the progress of a reaction.

6
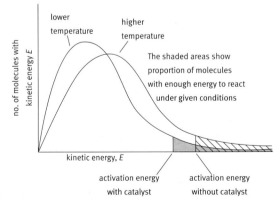

# Chapter 11

1   a   $CuSO_4 \cdot 5H_2O(s) \rightleftharpoons CuSO_4(s) + 5H_2O(l)$

---

    b   $NH_3(g) + HCl(g) \rightleftharpoons NH_4Cl(s)$
    c   $CaCO_3(s) + H_2O(l) + CO_2(g) \rightleftharpoons Ca(HCO_3)_2(aq)$

2   a   At 100 °C and atmospheric pressure.
    b   Salt crystals mixed with a saturated solution.

3   a   They are not closed systems. Fresh reactant gas steadily flows in and product gases keep flowing out.
    b   In a closed container at a constant temperature.

4
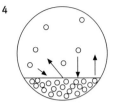

5   a   Turns orange on adding acid.
    b   Turns yellow on adding alkali.

6   a   Equilibrium shifts to the right converting more methane to CO and $H_2$.
    b   Equilibrium shifts to the left reducing the number of molecules.
    c   Equilibrium shifts to the right – the direction of change which is endothermic.

7   $2SO_2(g) + O_2(g) \rightleftharpoons 2SO_3(g)$ exothermic
    The reaction is exothermic so the yield falls at equilibrium as the temperature rises, therefore cooling increases the yield. Adding a reactant (oxygen) and removing a product (sulfur trioxide) both tend to make the equilibrium shift to the right.

8   Sulfur oxides are acidic and form sulfuric acid in moist air. This produces acid rain, which damages health, corrodes buildings and pollutes the environment.

9   a   Raising the pressure and not allowing the temperature to rise too high (the higher the temperature the lower the yield at equilibrium).
    b   Using a catalyst and increasing the pressure, which concentrates the gases and raises the temperature.

10  a   $2NH_3(aq) + H_2SO_4(aq) \rightarrow (NH_4)_2SO_4(aq)$
        $NH_3(aq) + HNO_3(aq) \rightarrow NH_4NO_3(aq)$
    b   Acid-base reactions. Ammonia is a base.
    c   They are used as fertilisers. Ammonium salts supply nitrates for plant growth.

11  $N_2 \rightarrow NH_3 \rightarrow NO \rightarrow NO_2 \rightarrow HNO_3 \rightarrow NH_4NO_3$
    0    −3    +2    +4    +5    −3 +5

# Chapter 12

1   Alkenes: $C_6H_{12}$

2   $C_nH_{(2n+2)}O$

3   Both: $C_{11}H_{14}O_2$

4   a   $C_6H_{12}$
    b   $C_4H_8O$

5   a   2,2-dimethylpropane
    b   butane
    c   2-methylpropan-1-ol
    d   butanal

---

**6 a**

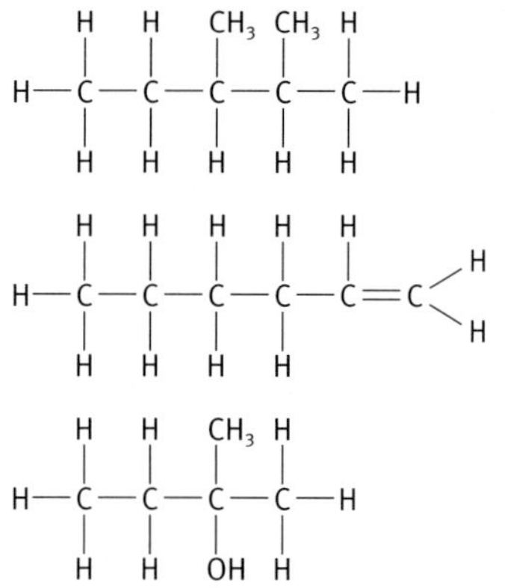

**7**

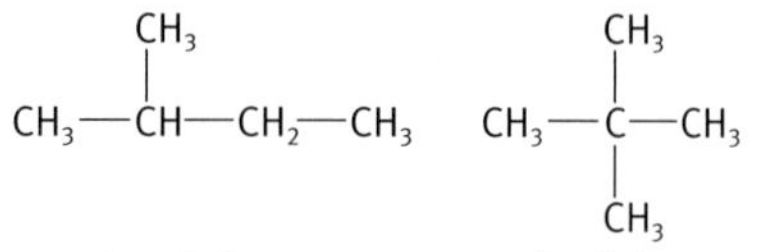

2-methylbutane      2,2-dimethylpropane

also pentane

**8**

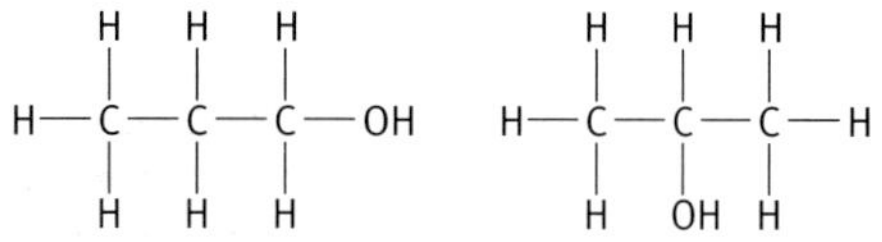

propan-1-ol      propan-2-ol

**9**

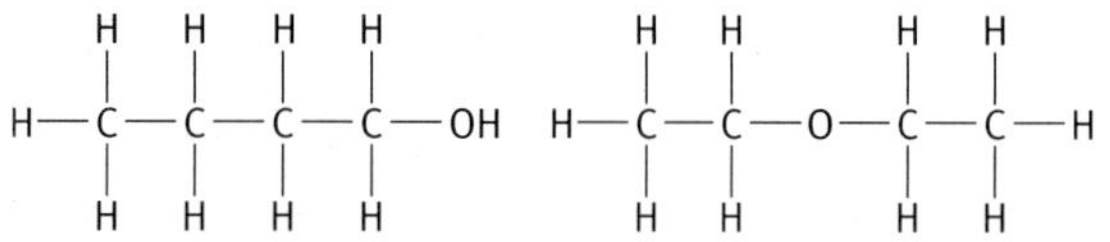

butan-1-ol      ethoxyethane

**10**

*cis* 1,2-dichloroethene      *trans* 1,2-dichloroethene

# Chapter 13

**1**

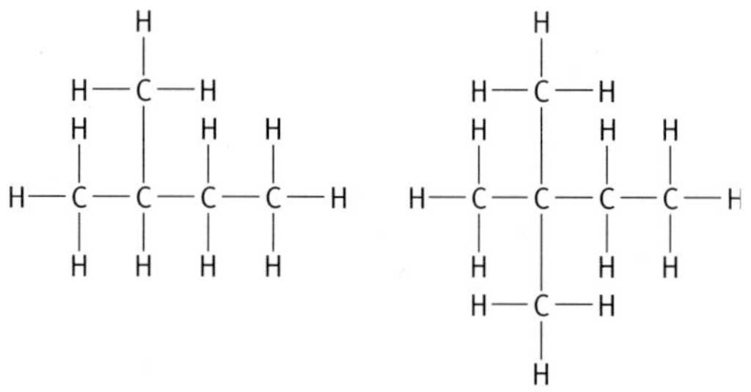

**2**

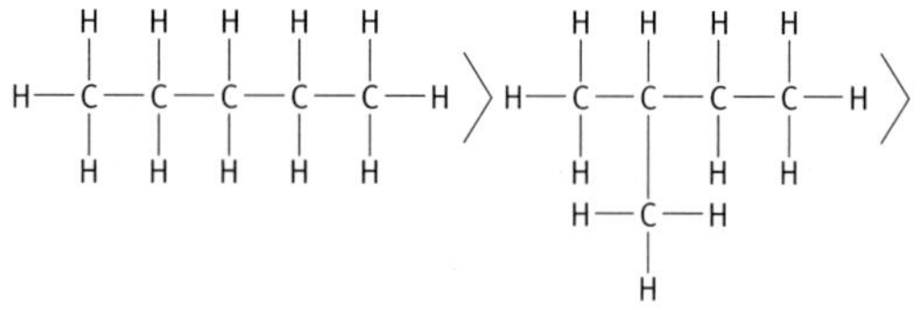

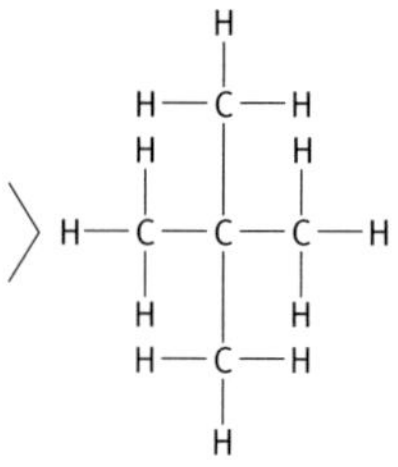

**3 a** $2C_2H_6(g) + 7O_2(g) \rightarrow 4CO_2(g) + 6H_2O(l)$

  **b** $C_2H_6(g) + Cl_2(g) \rightarrow C_2H_5Cl(g) + HCl(g)$

  **c** $C_2H_6(g) \rightarrow C_2H_4(g) + H_2(g)$

**4**

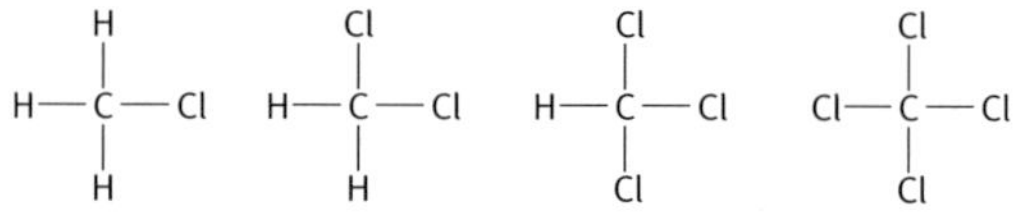

chloromethane   dichloromethane   trichloromethane   tetrachloromethane

**5** One of the termination steps involves two methyl free radicals combining to form ethane.

**6** See page 78. The same steps but with $Cl_2$ or $Cl$ in place of $Br_2$ or $Br$.

**7** $C_2H_6 \rightarrow C_2H_5\bullet + H\bullet$

**8**

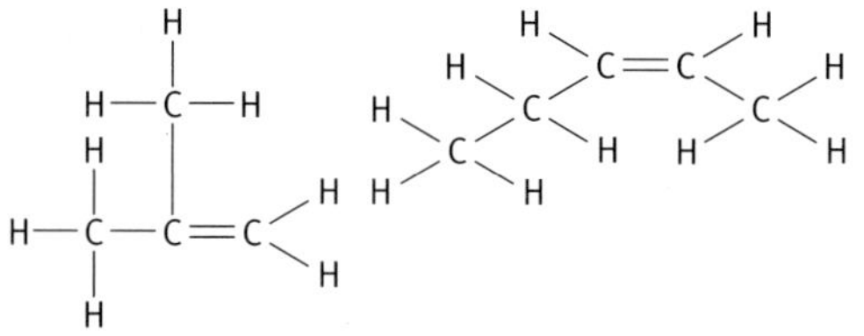

**9 a** $CH_3-CH=CH_2(g) + H_2(g) \rightarrow CH_3-CH_2-CH_3(g)$

    At room temperature with a Pt or Pd catalyst or on heat to about 140 °C with a Ni catalyst.

  **b** $CH_3-CH=CH-CH_3(g) + Br_2(l) \rightarrow CH_3-CHBr-CHBr-CH_3(l)$

    Reaction with bromine at room temperature.

  **c** $C_2H_5-CH=CH_2(g) + HBr(g) \rightarrow CH_3-CH_2-CHBr-CH_3(l)$

    Reaction with hydrogen bromide at room temperature.

**10**

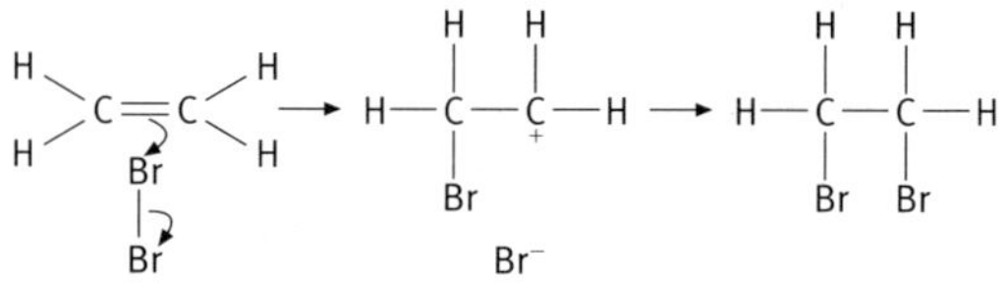

**11 a**

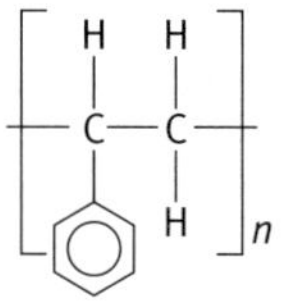

poly(phenylethene)

  **b**

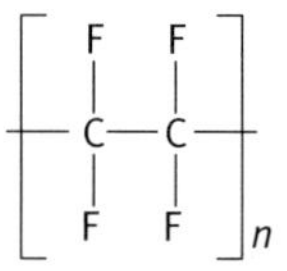

poly(tetrafluoroethene)

# Chapter 14

1  a  $CH_3-CH_2-CH_2-CH_2-CH_2Cl$
      primary

   b  $CH_3-\underset{\underset{Br}{|}}{\overset{\overset{CH_3}{|}}{C}}-CH_3$

      tertiary

   c  $CH_3-CH_2-\underset{\underset{I}{|}}{CH}-CH_3$

      secondary

2  Polar: $CHCl_3$, $CH_2Br_2$, $CHI_3$

3  Order of boiling points: 1-chlorobutane >
   2-chlorobutane > 2-chloro-2-methylpropane
   All three molecules have the same number of atoms
   and electrons, so they are comparable. Branching makes
   a molecule shorter and more compact. This decreases
   the surface area over which intermolecular forces can
   act.

4  a  $CH_3-CH_2Br(g) + OH^-(aq) \rightarrow CH_3-CH_2OH(aq) + Br^-(aq)$
      Heat under reflux with aqueous sodium hydroxide.

   b  $CH_3-CH_2Br(g) + CN^-(aq) \rightarrow CH_3-CH_2CN(l) + Br^-(aq)$
      $CH_3-CH_2CN(l) + H^+(aq) + 2H_2O(l)$
      $\qquad\qquad \rightarrow CH_3-CH_2-CO_2H(aq) + NH_4^+(aq)$
      First heat under reflux with aqueous potassium cyanide.
      Isolate the product and then heat under reflux with dilute
      hydrochloric acid.

   c  $CH_3-CH_2-CH_2Cl(l) + NH_3(\text{in ethanol})$
      $\qquad\qquad \rightarrow CH_3-CH_2-CH_2NH_2(l) + HCl(aq)$
      Heat the halogeno compound with the reagent in a
      sealed tube. Note the two products combine to form a
      salt: $CH_3-CH_2-CH_2NH_3Cl(l)$

   d  $CH_3-CH(CH_3)Br-CH_3(l) + OH^-(\text{in ethanol})$
      $\rightarrow CH_3-C(CH_3)=CH_2(l) + Br^-(aq) + H_2O(l)$
      Heat under reflux with a solution of potassium hydroxide
      in ethanol.

5  $OH^-$, $CN^-$, $NH_3$ they all have a lone pair of electrons which
   can form a new covalent bond with the carbon atom
   originally attached to the halogen atom.

6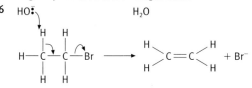

   The $OH^-$ accepts $H^+$ (a proton) forming water

# Chapter 15

1  a  $CH_3-\underset{\underset{OH}{|}}{\overset{\overset{CH_3}{|}}{C}}-CH_2-CH_3$   tertiary

   b  $CH_3-CH_2-\overset{\overset{CH_3}{|}}{CH}-CH_2OH$   primary

   c  $CH_3-\underset{\underset{OH}{|}}{CH}-\overset{\overset{CH_3}{|}}{CH}-CH_3$   secondary

2  $H-O-H + Na \rightarrow NaOH + {}^1/_2H_2(g)$
   $C_2H_5-O-H + Na \rightarrow NaOC_2H_5 + {}^1/_2H_2(g)$
   Both produce hydrogen gas, which burns with a pop.

3  Hydrogen chloride – a colourless fuming gas, which turns
   litmus red and forms a white smoke with ammonia fumes.

4  a  The O–H bond
   b  The C–O bond
   c  The C–O bond

5  a  $CH_3-CH_2-CH_2OH(l) + HI(g) \rightarrow CH_3-CH_2-CH_2I(l) + H_2O(l)$
      Mix the alcohol with a mixture of red phosphorus and
      iodine, which produces hydrogen iodide in the presence
      of moisture.

   b  $CH_3-CH_2-CH_2OH(l) \rightarrow CH_3-CH=CH_2(g) + H_2O(l)$
      Pass the vapour over hot aluminium oxide.

   c  $CH_3-CH_2-CH_2OH(l) + [O] \rightarrow CH_3-CH_2-CHO(l) + H_2O(l)$
      Warm with acidified potassium dichromate(VI) and distil
      off the product as it forms.

   d  $CH_3-CH_2-CH_2OH(l) + CH_3CO_2H(l) \rightarrow CH_3CO_2C_3H_7(l) + H_2O(l)$
      Warm a mixture of the alcohol and the acid with a few
      drops of concentrated sulfuric acid to act as a catalyst.

6  $CH_3-CH_2-CH_2-CHO(l) + 2[H]$
   $\qquad\qquad \rightarrow CH_3-CH_2-CH_2-CH_2OH(l) + H_2O(l)$

7  $CH_2=CH_2(g) + H_2O(l) \rightarrow CH_3-CH_2OH(l)$
   Pass ethene and steam over a phosphoric acid catalyst.

8  $2CH_3OH(l) + 3O_2(g) \rightarrow 2CO_2(g) + 4H_2O(l)$

# Chapter 16

1  Like a fossil, it formed millions of years ago when the dead
   remains of living organisms died, were buried under
   sediments and then altered by heat and pressure.

2  Sulfur in the fuel turns to sulfur dioxide, which is an acidic
   oxide and contributes to acid rain. In moist air, sulfur dioxide
   reacts with water and oxygen to form sulfuric acid.

3  Methane ($27\,800$ kJ kg$^{-1}$) > methanol ($22\,700$ kJ kg$^{-1}$)

4  In any small vehicle or vessel where the space taken up by
   the fuel is more significant than its mass.

5  $C(s) + O_2(g) \rightarrow CO_2(g)$

6  The intermediates are ionic. Bond breaking is heterolytic.

7  a  $CH_3-CH_2-CH_2-CH_2-CH_2-CH_2-CH_2-CH_2-CH_2-CH_3 \rightarrow$

      $CH_3-\overset{\overset{CH_3}{|}}{CH}-CH_2-CH_2-\overset{\overset{CH_3}{|}}{CH}-CH_3 + CH_2=CH_2$

   b  $CH_3-CH_2-CH_2-CH_2-CH_3 \longrightarrow CH_3-\overset{\overset{CH_3}{|}}{CH}-CH_2-CH_3$

   c  $CH_3-CH_2-CH_2-CH_2-CH_2-CH_2-CH_3 \longrightarrow$ [benzene ring with $CH_3$] $+ 4H_2$

8

$$CH_3$$
$$|$$
$$O$$
$$|$$
$$CH_3-C-CH_3$$
$$|$$
$$CH_3$$

9 The intermediates are free radicals. Bond breaking is homolytic.

10

11 The normal bond angles for four bonds round a carbon atom are 109.5°. One way to account for the reactivity of epoxyethane is to think of the triangle of bonds with 60° bond angles as being strained.

12

## Chapter 17

1 A primary pollutant is a chemical released directly into the air by the source of pollution such a sulfur dioxide from burning coal. A secondary pollutant forms as a result of chemical reactions involving the chemicals released into the air together with oxygen or water vapour. An example is sulfuric acid, which forms when sulfur dioxide reacts with oxygen and water.

2 Sulfur dioxide produces sulfuric acid which falls as acid rain. It corrodes metals and reacts with calcium carbonate in building stone, such as limestone.

3 Catalytic converters free exhaust gases of oxides of nitrogen, which both contribute to acid rain and help to form photochemical smog. The converters have no effect on carbon dioxide so they do nothing to reduce the problem of global warming. They may even make the problem a little worse by increasing fuel consumption.

4 There is a great variety of plastics that are hard to identify and separate. The properties of recycled plastics are, in most cases, inferior to the original material. Plastics have low density so they are very bulky. Transport costs can be high in relation to the value of the plastic. It may often be better to burn plastics as fuels than to recycle them.

## Chapter 18

1 a By collecting the hydrogen in a gas syringe or in a measuring cylinder over water and recording the volume of gas at regular intervals.

b Using the colorimeter to follow the disappearance of the colour of orange-yellow iodine as colourless products form.

c By withdrawing samples from the regular intervals and titrating with sodium hydroxide solution to find the concentration of the ethanoic acid formed.

d By using a conductivity cell and meter to track the increase in conductivity of the solution as molecules react to form ions.

2 It takes 4 half-lives to fall from $200 \times 10^{-4}$ mol dm$^{-3}$ to $12.5 \times 10^{-4}$ mol dm$^{-3}$, which is 4800 s.

3 a Rate = $k[H_2][NO]^2$

b $k = 0.384$ mol$^{-2}$ dm$^6$ s$^{-1}$

c Halving the hydrogen concentration halves the rate.

d Doubling the NO concentration increases the rate by a factor of 4.

4 a The initial rate = $2.25 \times 10^{-5}$ mol dm$^{-3}$ s$^{-1}$

b The half-life = 650 s.

5 a NO – second order, CO – zero order, O$_2$ – zero order

b Rate = $k[NO(g)]^2$

c $k = 440$ mol$^{-1}$ dm$^3$ s$^{-1}$

6 As $T$ increases the $-E_a/RT$ term in the equation becomes less negative, so ln$k$ and therefore $k$ increase.

7 At a higher temperature the distribution shifts (to the right in Figure 10.05 on page 65) in a way which increases the number of molecules that can collide with energy greater than the activation energy for reaction.

8 The larger the value of $E_a$, the more negative the value of the $-E_a/RT$ term and so the smaller ln$k$ and hence the smaller the value of $k$.

9 a $NO_2(g) + CO(g) \rightarrow NO(g) + CO_2(g)$

b The first step.

## Chapter 19

1 a $K_c = \dfrac{[SO_3(g)]^2}{[SO_2(g)]^2[O_2(g)]}$ Units: mol$^{-1}$ dm$^3$

b $K_c = \dfrac{[CH_3CO_2C_2H_5(l)][H_2O(l)]}{[CH_3CO_2H(l)][C_2H_5OH(l)]}$ Units: none

c $K_c = \dfrac{[CuCl_4^-(aq)]}{[Cu^{2+}(aq)][Cl^-(aq)]^4}$ Units: mol$^{-4}$ dm$^{12}$

2 $K_c = 0.165$ mol$^{-2}$ dm$^6$

3 $K_c = 0.2$ mol$^2$ dm$^{-3}$

4 $K_p = 38.1$ kPa

5 $K_p = 3.89 \times 10^{-5}$

6 a $K_c = \dfrac{[H_2(g)]^4}{[H_2O(g)]^4}$

b $K_c = \dfrac{[Fe^{2+}(aq)][Ag^+(aq)]}{[Fe^{3+}(aq)]}$

7 a The equilibrium shifts to the right. All concentration (or pressure) terms in the expression for $K$ increase by the same factor. This factor appears squared on the top of the expression but raised to the power 4 on the bottom. So at the moment the pressure increases the expression is too small and no longer equals $K$. A shift to the right increases the concentration terms on the top of the expression and decreases those on the bottom until its value again equals $K$.

b Unaffected by changes of pressure. Changing the pressure changes the two terms on the top of the expression for $K$ by the same factor as the two terms on the bottom. The factor cancels .

8 $K_p$ becomes larger as the temperature rises, so the equilibrium shifts to the right as the temperature rises. So the forward reaction is endothermic.

9 $K_p$ becomes smaller as the temperature rises, so the equilibrium shifts to the left as the temperature rises. So the reaction of hydrogen with iodine is exothermic.

# Chapter 20

1 a The oxide ion is the base that accepts two protons from oxonium ions in dilute sulfuric acid

   b The ammonia molecule is the base that accepts a proton from an oxonium ions in dilute nitric acid.

   c The hydroxide ion is the base that accepts a proton from an ammonium ion.

   d The carbonate ion is the base that accepts protons from oxonium ions in dilute hydrochloric acid forming first the hydrocarbonate ion and then carbonic acid.

2 Nitrate ion, ethanoate ion, hydrogensulfate ion, carbonate ion.

3 Water, ammonium ion, carbonic acid.

4 a $0.01$ mol dm$^{-3}$

   b $2.0 \times 10^{-4}$ mol dm$^{-3}$

   c $6.3 \times 10^{-10}$ mol dm$^{-3}$

5 a pH $= 1$

   b pH $= 2.3$

   c pH $= 14$

   d pH $= 12.3$

6 a $0.1$ mol dm$^{-3}$

   b $1 \times 10^{-13}$ mol dm$^{-3}$

7 pH $= 2.4$

8 pH $= 2.9$

9 pH $= 5.9$

10 a chlorethanoic > ethanoic > carbonic > phenol

   b chlorethanoic and ethanoic acids

11 a B

   b C

   c A

   d D

12 A strong base is fully ionised and so has a higher OH$^-$ concentration than a weak base. The higher the OH$^-$ concentration, the lower the $H_3O^+$ concentration and hence the higher the pH.

13 $pK_a \approx 4.5$ so $K_a = 3.2 \times 10^{-5}$ mol dm$^{-3}$

14 Take the example of ethanoic acid with sodium hydroxide. At the equivalence point the salt formed is sodium ethanoate. The ethanoate ion is the conjugate base of a weak acid. So a solution of sodium ethanoate is alkaline.

15 A – methyl red/bromothymol blue

   B – phenolphthalein

   C – methyl red

   D – no indicator suitable

16 pH low. $[H_3O^+]$ high. Equilibrium shifts in favour of HIn. pH high. $[H_3O^+]$ low. Equilibrium shifts in favour of In$^-$.

17 To show this, note that log $10 = +1$ and that log $0.1 = -1$.

18 Blood is buffered by haemoglobin. Eye lotions and drops are buffered so that they have the same pH as tears (which are also buffer systems). Swimming pools are buffered by a mixture of hydrogencarbonate and carbonate ions.

19 Adding acid to a buffer mixture increases the $H_3O^+$ concentration. The equilibrium shifts in the direction that removes oxonium ions, thus tending to counteract the change in pH. Adding alkali decreases the $H_3O^+$ concentration. The equilibrium shifts in the direction that produces oxonium ions, again tending to counteract the change in pH.

20 pH $= 4$

21 Part way to the end-point the weak acid is partly converted to its salt. So the flask contains a mixture of the weak acid and its salt, which make a buffer solution.

22 Note that in a buffer there are relatively large amounts of the weak acid and its salt, so they determine the pH. During a titration, only a drop or two of indicator is added, so the pH is determined by the titration mixture in the flask.

# Chapter 21

1 a $Fe(s) \rightarrow Fe^{2+}(aq) + 2e^-$

   $2Ag^+(aq) + 2e^- \rightarrow 2Ag(s)$

   b $Fe(s) \mid Fe^{2+}(aq) \vdots Ag^+(aq) \mid Ag(s)$

2 a $Ni^{2+}(aq) + 2e^- \rightarrow Ni(s)$    $E^{\ominus} = -0.25$ V

   b $Cu^{2+}(aq) + 2e^- \rightarrow Cu(s)$    $E^{\ominus} = +0.34$ V

   c $Al^{3+}(aq) + 3e^- \rightarrow Al(s)$    $E^{\ominus} = -1.67$ V

3

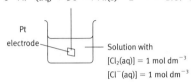

4 a Chlorine molecules

   b Sodium atoms

   c Order of strength as oxidising agents: chlorine > bromine > iodine

   d Metals act as reducing agents: in the table sodium is the most reactive and copper the least reactive of the metals shown.

5 a $Mg(s) + Cu^{2+}(aq) \rightarrow Mg^{2+}(aq) + Cu(s)$

   b No reaction

   c $2Al(s) + 6H^+(aq) \rightarrow 2Al^{3+}(aq) + 3H_2(g)$ but slow – oxide film on Al metal

   d No reaction

   e $Cl_2(aq) + 2I^-(aq) \rightarrow 2Cl^-(aq) + I_2(aq)$

6 Hydrogen peroxide tends to disproportionate giving off oxygen gas. In other words, it decomposes into water and oxygen. This is normally slow except in the presence of a catalyst, such as manganese(IV) oxide or the enzyme catalase.

7 $Au(s) \mid Au^{3+}(aq) \vdots Au^+(aq) \mid Au(s)$

   $3Au^+(aq) \rightarrow 2Au(s) + Au^{3+}(aq)$

   $E_{cell} = (+1.69) - (+1.40)$

   $= 0.29$ V

8 a Positive electrode: lead coated with lead(IV) oxide, $PbO_2$

   Negative electrode: lead metal

   Electrolyte: dilute sulfuric acid

   b $Pb(s) + PbO_2(s) + 2SO_4^{2-}(aq) + 4H^+(aq) \rightarrow$

   $2PbSO_4(s) + 2H_2O(l)$

   c e.m.f $= 2.05$ V

   d Six cells connected in series give a 12 V battery.

   e The half equations are the reverse of the two equations when the cell is delivering current. An important feature of the cell is that, as it discharges, the products at both electrodes are insoluble lead sulfate. The lead sulfate does not dissolve or turn to a gas and so move away from the electrodes; instead it stays in contact with the electrodes so that the electrode processes can easily be reversed.

9 The oxygen electrode system is more positive than the $Fe^{2+}(aq) \mid Fe(s)$ electrode, so oxygen tends to oxidise iron to iron(II).

10 Zinc and magnesium are more powerful reducing agents than iron. So long as one of these metals is present it keeps the iron reduced to the metal, itself being oxidised instead. Effectively a cell is set up such as $Zn(s) \mid Zn^{2+}(aq) \vdots Fe^{2+}(aq) \mid Fe(s)$ in which the right-hand electrode is the cathode. Oxidation happens at the anode, so it is the zinc that corrodes. Tin is a less powerful reducing agent than iron and so cannot give cathodic protection.

## Chapter 22

1 a $\Delta H_1$ – standard enthalpy change of formation of magnesium chloride

   $\Delta H_2$ – enthalpy change of atomisation of magnesium

   $\Delta H_3$ – first ionisation enthalpy of magnesium

   $\Delta H_4$ – second ionisation enthalpy of magnesium

   $\Delta H_5$ – 2 × enthalpy change of atomisation of chlorine

   $\Delta H_6$ – 2 × electron affinity of chlorine

   b Lattice enthalpy = $-2522$ kJ mol$^{-1}$

2 a Lattice enthalpy of MgCl (estimated from theory)

   Enthalpy change of atomisation of chlorine (experimental)

   Electron affinity of chlorine (experimental)

   Enthalpy change of atomisation of magnesium (experimental)

   First ionisation enthalpy of magnesium (experimental)

   b Calculated value for standard enthalpy of formation of MgCl(s) = $-95$ kJ mol$^{-1}$

   c $\Delta H^\ominus = -452$ kJ mol$^{-1}$

   d The enthalpy change for the reaction shows that MgCl(s) is unstable relative to decomposition to $MgCl_2$(s).

3 a Iodide ions are larger than fluoride ions, so the same charges (1+ and 1−) are further apart and the attraction between them is therefore smaller.

   b Bonding in LiF nearer to the ionic ideal than in LiI. The fluoride ion is the most electronegative element so electron transfer is most complete in compounds of metals with this element. The iodide ion is larger and more polarisable, so a degree of electron sharing is more likely in LiI.

4 Charges in all compounds are 2+ and 2−, so differences are due to ion size. The smaller the ions, the larger the lattice enthalpy.

   MgO    $-3791$ kJ mol$^{-1}$

   MgS    $-3299$ kJ mol$^{-1}$

   BaO    $-3054$ kJ mol$^{-1}$

   BaS    $-2725$ kJ mol$^{-1}$

5 In a series of similar compounds with the same structure and ionic charges, lattice enthalpies vary with the sum of the ionic radii. Hydration enthalpies vary with the individual ionic radii. In Group 2 compounds with a large anion, such as the sulfate ion, the increasing size of the metal ion means that the hydration enthalpy decreases faster down the group than the lattice enthalpy. With a large anion, the sum of the ionic radii is affected less in proportion because its value is largely determined by the large size of the sulfate ion. So the salts get less soluble.

   In Group 2 compounds with a small anion, such as the hydroxide ion, the increasing size has a much more significant effect on the sum of the ionic radii. With a small anion, the lattice energy is much more sensitive to the size of the cation and it is the lattice enthalpy that decreases most as the metal ion size increases down the group. So the salts get more soluble down the group.

## Chapter 23

1 In its everyday sense a spontaneous change is one that just happens. Spontaneous people act on impulse. In the chemist's sense, a spontaneous change is one that tends to go – even if there is some sort of barrier that means that, in fact, it goes very slowly or not at all.

2 In a gas there are many more ways of distributing the free and fast moving molecules and their energy than there are in a solid, where the atoms or molecules have fixed positions.

carbon (diamond) $S^\ominus = 2.4$ J mol$^{-1}$ K$^{-1}$

iron $S^\ominus = 30.0$ J K$^{-1}$ mol$^{-1}$

water $S^\ominus = 69.9$ J K$^{-1}$ mol$^{-1}$

steam $S^\ominus = 188.7$ J K$^{-1}$ mol$^{-1}$

methane $S^\ominus = 186.2$ J K$^{-1}$ mol$^{-1}$

3 Temperature 298 K and pressure 100 kPa.

4 a $\Delta S^\ominus = -220$ J K$^{-1}$ mol$^{-1}$

   $\Delta H^\ominus = -91$ kJ mol$^{-1}$ = $-91\,000$ J mol$^{-1}$

   b $\Delta G = \Delta H - T\Delta S$

   Assuming that $\Delta S$ and $\Delta H$ do not vary with temperature and that the pressure is constant, $\Delta G = 0$ when:

   $\Delta H = T\Delta S$, that is when:

   $T = \Delta H \div \Delta S = (-91\,000$ J mol$^{-1}) \div (-220$ J K$^{-1}$ mol$^{-1})$

   So there is not tendency for the reaction to go when

   $T = 414$ K

5 a standard electrode potentials

   b $K_p$

   c $K_a$

   d $K_p$

   e $K_c$

6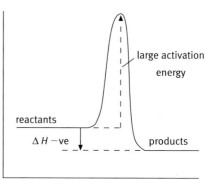

7 $H_2O$ at room temperature does not decompose into its elements. $N_2O$ at room temperature does not decompose into its elements. $NH_4Cl$ at room temperature does not decompose into ammonia and hydrogen chloride.

$H_2O_2$ in solution at room temperature in the presence of manganese(IV) oxide catalyst rapidly decomposes into water and oxygen.

8 Since the reactants and products are all solids, the changes in entropy values are likely to be small. So $T\Delta S$ is likely to be small compared to the large lattice enthalpies and ionisation enthalpies.

## Chapter 24

1 $2Na(s) + 2H_2O(l) \rightarrow 2NaOH(aq) + H_2(g)$

   Na oxidised to the +1 state.

   $Mg(s) + H_2O(l) \rightarrow MgO(s) + H_2(g)$

   Mg oxidised to the +2 state.

   $2Al(s) + 3H_2O(l) \rightarrow Al_2O_3(s) + 3H_2(g)$

   Al oxidised to the +3 state.

   $Cl_2(aq) + H_2O(l) \rightarrow HCl(aq) + HOCl(aq)$

   Cl disproportionates to the +1 and −1 states.

2 a $Na_2O(s) + H_2O(l) \rightarrow 2NaOH(aq)$

   b $MgO(s) + H_2O(l) \rightarrow Mg(OH)_2(s)$

   c $SO_2(g) + H_2O(l) \rightarrow H_2SO_3(aq)$

   d $P_2O_3(g) + 3H_2O(l) \rightarrow 2H_3PO_3(aq)$

3 a $[Al(H_2O)_6]^{3+}$ – water molecules bonded to the highly-polarising aluminium ion are acidic and donate protons to free water molecules. So a solution containing hydrated aluminium ions is acidic.

**b** $[Al(H_2O)_3(OH)_3](s)$ – adding alkali to a solution of aluminium ions removes further protons to form this uncharged complex, which is insoluble in water. The precipitate dissolves in acid, which re-protonates the $OH^-$ ions forming $[Al(H_2O)_6]^{3+}$ again.

**c** $[Al(H_2O)_2(OH)_4]^-$ – the precipitate of $[Al(H_2O)_3(OH)_3](s)$ also redissolves in excess alkali, which removes another proton from another bonded water molecule producing this negative ion. This process can be reversed by adding acid.

**4** $SiO_2$ reacts with the basic oxide CaO to form a salt $CaSiO_4$ which separates as a liquid slag at the temperature of the furnace.

**5** Hydration of metal ions: polar water molecules cluster round and bond to the dissolved ions.
Hydrolysis of a chloride: the chloride splits into two new compounds when it reacts with water.

**6** $PCl_3(l) + 3H_2O(l) \rightarrow H_3PO_3(aq) + 3HCl(aq)$

**7** See question 3a.
$[Al(H_2O)_6]^{3+} + H_2O(l) \rightarrow [Al(H_2O)_5OH]^{2+} + H_3O^+(aq)$

**8 a** $CO_2(g) + H_2O(l) \rightarrow H_2CO_3(aq)$

**b** $SnO(s) + 2H_3O^+(aq) \rightarrow Sn^{2+}(aq) + 3H_2O(l)$
$SnO(s) + H_2O(l) + OH^-(aq) \rightarrow Sn(OH)_3^-(aq)$

**9** More negative: $Cl_2(aq) + 2e^- \rightarrow 2Cl^-(aq)$ $E = +1.36$ V
More positive: $PbO_2(s) + 4H^+(aq) + 2e^-$
$\rightarrow Pb^{2+}(aq) + 2H_2O(l)$ $E = +1.46$ V

**10**

**11** Similarities: colourless, non-polar liquids, immiscible in water.
Difference: $SiCl_4$ is rapidly hydrolysed by water while $CCl_4$ is inert.
Small size of carbon atom means that it is so entirely surrounded by the four chlorine atoms that a water molecule (the incoming nucleophile) cannot get to the $\delta+$ carbon atom. A silicon atom is larger so a water molecule can attack the central atom. Also, silicon, unlike carbon, has available empty d-orbitals in its outer third shell, which make it easy for the atom to accept a pair of electrons from the attacking nucleophile.

**12** $2Fe^{3+}(aq) + Sn^{2+}(aq) \rightarrow 2Fe^{2+}(aq) + Sn^{4+}(aq)$

# Chapter 25

**1** Sc – $1s^2 2s^2 2p^6 3s^2 3p^6 3d^1 4s^2$
V – $1s^2 2s^2 2p^6 3s^2 3p^6 3d^3 4s^2$
Cr – $1s^2 2s^2 2p^6 3s^2 3p^6 3d^5 4s^1$
Mn – $1s^2 2s^2 2p^6 3s^2 3p^6 3d^5 4s^2$
Fe – $1s^2 2s^2 2p^6 3s^2 3p^6 3d^6 4s^2$
Co – $1s^2 2s^2 2p^6 3s^2 3p^6 3d^7 4s^2$
Cu – $1s^2 2s^2 2p^6 3s^2 3p^6 3d^{10} 4s^1$

**2** The 3d and 4s energy orbitals differ only slightly in energy. Small variations can therefore affect the order in which orbitals fill. In chromium, the tendency for orbitals with similar energies to fill singly prevails, meaning that each of the 3d and the 4s orbitals has one electron. In copper, filling the 3d sub-shell is energetically the more favoured arrangement.

**3** $Sc^{3+}$ – $1s^2 2s^2 2p^6 3s^2 3p^6 3d^0 4s^0$
$Fe^{3+}$ – $1s^2 2s^2 2p^6 3s^2 3p^6 3d^5 4s^0$
$Fe^{2+}$ – $1s^2 2s^2 2p^6 3s^2 3p^6 3d^6 4s^0$
$Cu^{2+}$ – $1s^2 2s^2 2p^6 3s^2 3p^6 3d^9 4s^0$
$Cu^+$ – $1s^2 2s^2 2p^6 3s^2 3p^6 3d^{10} 4s^0$

**4** Scandium only forms compounds in the 3+ state, all of which are colourless. The $Sc^{3+}$ ion has no d-electrons. Sc is generally not counted as a transition metal.

**5** The +2 state becomes more stable relative to the +4 state across the series.
The highest oxidation state is achieved by magnesium in the middle of the row.
From Sc to Mn the highest common oxidation state corresponds to all the 3d and 4s electrons being involved in bonding.

**6** Zinc can reduce V(v) in stages to V(ii) then:
More negative: $Zn^{2+}(aq) + 2e^- \rightarrow Zn(s)$ $E^\ominus = -0.76$ V
More positive: $V^{3+}(aq) + e^- \rightarrow V^{2+}(aq)$ $E^\ominus = -0.26$ V
More negative: $Zn^{2+}(aq) + 2e^- \rightarrow Zn(s)$ $E^\ominus = -0.76$ V
More positive: $Cr^{3+}(aq) + e^- \rightarrow Cr^{2+}(aq)$ $E^\ominus = -0.41$ V

**7 a** The oxidation state of chromium in both ions is +6 so this is not a redox reaction.

**b** $2CrO_4^{2-}(aq) + 2H^+(aq) \rightleftharpoons Cr_2O_7^{2-}(aq) + H_2O(l)$
Adding acid increases $[H^+(aq)]$ and as a result the equilibrium shifts to the right.
Adding alkali decreases $[H^+(aq)]$ and as a result the equilibrium shifts to the left.

**8 a** Sulfur dioxide reduces orange dichromate(vi) to chromium(iii), which is green.

**b** Oxidation of a primary alcohol to an aldehyde and then to an acid.
Oxidation of a secondary alcohol to a ketone.

**9 a** $MnO_4^-(aq) + 8H^+(aq) + 5Fe^{2+}$
$\rightarrow Mn^{2+}(aq) + 4 H_2O(l) + 5Fe^{3+}$

**b** During the titration, the purple $MnO_4^-(aq)$ ions are reduced to almost colourless $Mn^{2+}(aq)$ ions. At the end-point addition of a drop of excess $MnO_4^-(aq)$, there is a permanent pink colour in the solution.

**c** 0.0675 mol dm$^{-3}$

**10** A more reactive metal such as zinc:
$Zn(s) + Cu^{2+} \rightarrow Zn^{2+}(aq) + Cu(s)$

**11** Monodentate: ammonia, water, cyanide ion, chloride ion
Bidentate: 1,2-diamminoethane, ethanedioate ion, any amino acid
Hexadentate: edta

**12 a** $[Ag(CN)_2]^-$

**b** $CuCl_4^{2-}$

**c** $[Fe(H_2O)_5SCN]^{2+}$

**13**

**14** Using en to represent 1,2-diaminoethane.
$Ni(NH_3)_6^{2+}(aq) + 3en(aq) \rightarrow Ni(en)_3^{2+}(aq) + 6NH_3(aq)$

**15 a** Cis-platin, an anticancer drug.

**b** The complex formed when fixer removes undeveloped silver from a photographic film or print.

**c** The complex in a solution used for silver plating.

**16**

**17 a** $[Co(H_2O)_6]^{2+}(aq) + 6Cl^-(aq) \rightarrow [CoCl_6]^{2-}(aq) + 6H_2O(l)$

**b** $[Fe(H_2O)_6]^{3+}(aq) + SCN^-(aq)$
$\rightarrow [Fe(H_2O)_5SCN]^{2+}(aq) + H_2O(l)$

**18** Cu(i) disproportionates to copper metal and copper(ii)

**19** Under standard conditions hydrogen peroxide will oxidise the reduced form of an electrode system that is less positive than +1.77 V. So it will oxidise $[Co(NH_3)_6]^{2+}(aq)$ but not $[Co(H_2O)_6]^{2+}(aq)$.

**20** Removing three protons from ligand water molecules produces an uncharged complex $[Cr(H_2O)_3(OH)_3](s)$, which is insoluble. Adding more alkali removes another proton so that the complex is again charged and it redissolves: $[Al(H_2O)_2(OH)_4]^-$.

**21** The $Fe^{3+}$ ion has a greater polarising power than the $Fe^{2+}$ ion, so hydrogen molecules in the iron(III) complex are more acidic.

**22** $M^{3+}$ ions are small and highly charged. The release of lattice energy when $M_2(CO_3)_3$ decomposes to $M_2O_3$ is high enough to more than compensate for the energy needed to break up the carbonate ion to an oxide ion and carbon dioxide. The higher the polarising power of the metal ion, the more unstable the carbonates.

**23** $NH_3(aq) + H_2O(l) \rightarrow NH_4^+(aq) + OH^-(aq)$
$Cu^{2+}(aq) + 2OH^-(aq) \rightarrow Cu(OH)_2(s)$
$Cu(OH)_2(s) + 4NH_3(aq) \rightarrow Cu(NH_3)_4^{2+}(aq) + 2OH^-(aq)$

**24** $\Delta E$, the size of the energy jump
h, Planck's constant
$\nu$, frequency of the radiation

**25** Peak absorption at around 520 nm. Colour purple.

**26** There is no possibility of electron transitions between d-orbitals in these ions since the d-orbitals are empty in $Sc^{3+}$ and full in $Zn^{2+}$ and $Cu^+$.

**27** The catalyst is in a separate phase, so it can be fixed in the reaction vessel as the reactants flow through or over it.

**28** The catalyst is expensive. The reactions take place on the surface of the catalyst. A finely divided catalyst has a larger surface area. Supporting the catalyst on an inert material allows a little catalyst to have a large surface area while being robust enough not to break up and be carried away in the exhaust gases.

**29** The catalyst has to be able to adsorb hydrogen to a significant extent to be effective but if it adsorbs the gas too strongly the hydrogen is not available for reaction. The effective catalysts are Ni, Pt and Pd.

**30** Use of acids or alkalis to hydrolyse esters, nitriles, peptides and amides.

**31** Persulfate ions can oxidise iron(II) to iron(III). Iron(III) can then oxidise iodide ions to iodine. The iron(II) is then available to be oxidised by persulfate ions again.

# Chapter 26

**1**

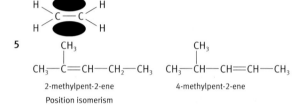

butane          2-methylpropane

**2**

$CH_3-C-CH_2-CH_3$ (with =O below C)          $CH_3CH_2CH_2CHO$

butanone          butanal

Functional group isomerism

**3** $CH_3CH_2CH_2CH_2Br$          $CH_3CH_2CHBrCH_3$

1-bromobutane          2-bromobutane

Chain and positional isomerism

$CH_3-CH(CH_3)-CH_2Br$          $CH_3-C(CH_3)(Br)-CH_3$

1-bromo-2-methylpropane          2-bromo-2-methylpropane

**4** The $\pi$ bond keeps the molecule planar and prevents rotation about the sigma bond.

**5** $CH_3-C(CH_3)=CH-CH_2-CH_3$          $CH_3-CH(CH_3)-CH=CH-CH_3$

2-methylpent-2-ene          4-methylpent-2-ene

Position isomerism

**6** See the answer to question 3, only 2-bromobutane is chiral.

$C_2H_5-C^*(H)(CH_3)-Br$

**7** $H_2N-C^*(CH_3)(H)-C(O)-N(H)-C^*(H)(CH_2SH)-CO_2H$

**8 a** amine, $CH_2OH$ alcohol
$H_2N-C(H)-CO_2H$ carboxylic acid
optical isomerism

**b** ketone, alkene
geometrical isomerism

**c** $CH_3-C(C_2H_5)(H)-Br$ halogenoalkane
optical isomerism

**d** $C_3H_7-C(CH_3)=CH-CO_2H$ alkene, carboxylic acid
geometrical isomerism

# Chapter 27

**1** $x = 120°, y = 109.5°, z = 120°$

**2** cyclohexene $+ H_2 \rightarrow$ cyclohexane   $\Delta H^\ominus = -120$ kJ mol$^{-1}$

**3 a** $C_4H_5$
**b** $C_8H_{10}$
**c**
$CH_3$ ... $CH_3$ ... $CH_3$

1,4-dimethylbenzene   1,3-dimethylbenzene   1,2-dimethylbenzene

**d** 1,4-dimethylbenzene

**e**

**4 a**

heat with conc H$_2$SO$_4$ + conc HNO$_3$

**b**

heat with AlCl$_3$ catalyst

**c**

heat with AlCl$_3$ catalyst

**5 a**

**b** Loss of a proton reforms the benzene ring stabilised by delocalised electrons.

**6 a** A Lewis acid is a species which accepts a pair of electrons.

**b**

electrophile

**c**

$Fe^{3+} + 6H_2O →$

**7 a** ethanoic acid > phenol > ethanol
**b** ethanoic acid

**8** Phenol and ethanol both react with sodium to form a sodium salt and hydrogen. Only phenol is acidic enough to react with aqueous sodium hydroxide to form a sodium salt.

# Chapter 28

**1** Oxidation: conversion of an aldehyde to a carboxylic acid with an acidic solution of dichromate(VI) ions.
Reduction: conversion of a ketone to a secondary alcohol with NaBH$_4$.
Addition: an aldehyde or ketone with HCN.

**2** The tertiary alcohol is not oxidised.

CH$_3$CHO    ethanal from ethanol

CH$_3$—CH—CHO (with CH$_3$)   2-methylpropanal from 2-methylpropan-1-ol

CH$_3$CH$_2$CH$_2$COCH$_3$   pentan-2-one from pentan-2-ol

**3 a** CH$_3$CHO + [O] → CH$_3$CO$_2$H
Heat under reflux with acidified potassium dichromate(VI).
**b** CH$_3$CH$_2$CHO + HCN → CH$_3$CH$_2$CHOHCN
Mix the aldehyde with an aqueous solution of potassium cyanide acidified with dilute hydrochloric acid.
**c** CH$_3$CH$_2$COCH$_3$ + 2[H] → CH$_3$CH$_2$CHOHCH$_3$
Mix with a solution in aqueous ethanol of NaBH$_4$.

**d** CH$_3$CH$_2$COCH$_3$ + HCN → CH$_3$CH$_2$CCH$_3$ (with OH and CN)
Mix the ketone with an aqueous solution of potassium cyanide acidified with dilute hydrochloric acid.

**4**

**5 a**

**b** A
**c** CH$_2$OH / CH$_2$OH   ethan-1,2-diol

**6 a** A solution of sodium chlorate(I) is alkaline. Chlorate(I) ions oxidise iodide ions to iodine. So the second reagent is chemically equivalent to the first.
**b** CH$_3$—C—CH$_3$ (with O)   propanone

# Chapter 29

**1**

**2 a** Butanoic acid
**b** Methanoic acid
**c** Butanoic acid

**3 a** CH$_3$CO$_2$H(aq) + NaOH(aq) → CH$_3$CO$_2^-$Na$^+$(aq) + H$_2$O(l)
Mix aqueous solutions of the reactants at room temperature. The product is sodium ethanoate.
**b** CH$_3$CO$_2$H(l) + C$_2$H$_5$OH(l) → CH$_3$CO$_2$C$_2$H$_5$(l) + H$_2$O(l)
Heat a mixture of the acid and the alcohol in the presence of a few drops of concentrated sulfuric acid. The product is ethyl ethanoate.
**c** CH$_3$CO$_2$H(l) + PCl$_5$(s) → CH$_3$COCl(l) + HCl(g) + POCl$_3$(l)
The reaction is rapid at room temperature. The product is ethanoyl chloride.
**d** CH$_3$CO$_2$H(l) + 4[H] → C$_2$H$_5$OH(l) + H$_2$O(l)
Warm with LiAlH$_4$ in dry ether. The product is ethanol.

**4**

X    Y

**5 a**

**b** Ethanoyl chloride is highly reactive and rapidly hydrolysed by moisture. Hydrolysis produces hydrogen chloride gas, which is a strong acid and highly corrosive. This makes it hazardous and difficult to store and process. Ethanoic anhydride is an alternative acylating agent, which is less reactive. It produces the liquid weak acid, ethanoic acid, when hydrolysed. It is less hazardous.

**6**

$$CH_3-C\overset{O}{\underset{NH_2}{\diagdown}} + HCl$$

**7**

**8** Butanoic acid, $CH_3CH_2CH_2CO_2H$, and propan-1-ol, $CH_3CH_2CH_2OH$.

**9**

**10** Alkaline hydrolysis produces a salt of the acid. The anion of the acid does not react directly with an alcohol.

**11** They are weak acids, so acidifying the salts with a strong acid, such as hydrochloric acid, produces the fatty acids.

**12 a** $CH_3(CH_2)_{16}CO_2H$
**b** $CH_3(CH_2)_4CH=CHCH_2CH=CH(CH_2)_7CO_2H$

# Chapter 30

**1**

**2 a** Both ammonia and amines have a reactive lone pair of electrons on the nitrogen atom.

**b** When a primary amine reacts with a halogenoalkane it produces a secondary amine, which also has a lone pair on the nitrogen. The product is also a nucleophile, which can react with more halogenoalkane. So a succession of substitution reactions is possible until a quaternary ammonium salt forms.

**3**

**4** A: Heat under reflux with KCN in ethanol
B: Heat under reflux with dilute hydrochloric acid
C: Add $PCl_5$ to the pure acid at room temperature
D: Add concentrated ammonia solution at room temperature
X: propanoic acid
Y: propanonitrile

**5 a** $CH_3CH_2NH_2(g) + H_2O(l) \rightleftharpoons CH_3CH_2NH_3^+(aq) + OH^-(aq)$
**b** $CH_3CH_2NH_2(g) + HCl(aq) \rightarrow CH_3CH_2NH_3^+(aq) + Cl^-(aq)$
**c** $CH_3COCl(l) + CH_3CH_2NH_2(g) \rightarrow CH_3CONHCH_2CH_3(s) + HCl(g)$

**6** Heat benzene with a mixture of concentrated nitric and sulfuric acids.

**7** $2KNO_3(s) \rightarrow 2KNO_2(s) + O_2(g)$

**8**

**9**

inductive effect makes $NH_2$ a stronger base

electron delocalisation stabilises phenylamine making it a weaker base

**10 a**

**b** There are two hydrogen atoms attached to the second carbon atom in glycine, so the molecule has a plane of symmetry. It is not chiral.

**11 a** $CH_2NH_2CO_2H(aq) + HCl(aq) \rightarrow CH_2NH_3^+CO_2H(aq) + Cl^-(aq)$
**b** $CH_2NH_2CO_2H(aq) + NaOH(aq)$
$$\rightarrow CH_2NH_2CO_2^-Na^+(aq) + H_2O(l)$$

**12** When a peptide bond forms, a small molecule of water is split off between the $-NH_2$ group in one molecule and the $-CO_2H$ group in another molecule. This is an example of a condensation reaction.

# Chapter 31

**1 a** Phenylethene polymerises to poly(phenylethene)

**b** Propenonitrile polymerises to poly(propenonitrile)

**2 a** Tetrafluoroethene

**b** Methyl 2-methylpropenoate

**3**

**4** In homolytic fission a covalent bond breaks so that each atom retains one electron of the shared pair, forming a free radical.

**5**

**6** When a peptide bond forms, a small molecule of water is split off between the $-NH_2$ group in one molecule and the $-CO_2H$ group in another molecule. This is an example of a condensation reaction. Forming a series of peptide bonds produces a condensation polymer.

**7 a**

**b**

**8 a** Plastics in landfill will decompose in landfill if they are biodegradable, plastic discarded as litter will not remain as a hazard to wildlife.

**b** Condensation polymers because ester and amide bonds can be split by hydrolysis. The backbone of addition polymers is a chain of carbon–carbon bonds which resists attack by aqueous reagents.

**9** Hydrogen bonding is possible between the N—H groups and the oxygen atoms of C=O groups in neighbouring chains.

## Chapter 32

**1 a**

$$CH_3CH_2CH_2Br \xrightarrow[\text{heat}]{\text{NaOH(aq)}} CH_3CH_2CH_2OH \xrightarrow[\text{heat}]{Cr_2O_7^{2-}/H^+}$$
$$\cdot\ CH_3CH_2CO_2$$

**b**

$$C_3H_7{-}OH \xrightarrow[\text{heat}]{\text{NaBr} \atop \text{conc } H_2SO_4} C_3H_7Br \xrightarrow[\text{heat}]{\text{KCN} \atop H^+}$$
$$C_3H_7CN \xrightarrow[\text{in dry ether}]{LiAlH_4} C_3H_7CH_2NH_2$$

**c**

$$C_2H_5{-}OH \xrightarrow[\text{heat}]{\text{NaBr} \atop \text{conc } H_2SO_4} C_2H_5Br \xrightarrow[\text{heat}]{\text{KCN} \atop H^+}$$
$$C_2H_5CN \xrightarrow[\text{heat}]{H^+/H_2O} C_2H_5CO_2H$$

**d**

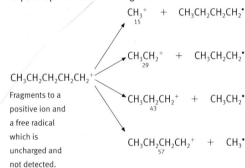

**2** X: ethanal
Y: 2-hydroxypropanoic acid
Step 1: warm with acidified potassium dichromate(VI)
Step 2: mix with KCN acidified with hydrochloric acid to form HCN
Step 3: heat under reflux with dilute hydrochloric acid
Step 4: heat with moderately concentrated sulfuric acid

**3 a**

$$CH_3{-}\overset{\overset{\displaystyle CH_3}{|}}{\underset{\underset{\displaystyle H}{|}}{C}}{-}Mg{-}Br \xrightarrow[\text{(2) } H_2O/H^+]{\text{(1) } \overset{CH_3}{\underset{H}{>}}C{=}O} CH_3{-}\overset{\overset{\displaystyle CH_3}{|}}{\underset{\underset{\displaystyle H}{|}}{C}}{-}\overset{\overset{\displaystyle CH_3}{|}}{\underset{\underset{\displaystyle H}{|}}{C}}{-}OH$$

**b**

$$CH_3{-}\overset{\overset{\displaystyle CH_3}{|}}{\underset{\underset{\displaystyle CH_3}{|}}{C}}{-}Mg{-}Cl \xrightarrow[\text{(2) } H_2O/H^+]{\text{(1) } CO_2(\text{dry ice})} CH_3{-}\overset{\overset{\displaystyle CH_3}{|}}{\underset{\underset{\displaystyle CH_3}{|}}{C}}{-}CO_2H$$

**c**

$$CH_3CH_2CH_2{-}Mg{-}Br \xrightarrow[\text{(2) } H_2O/H^+]{\text{(1) } \overset{CH_3}{\underset{CH_3}{>}}C{=}O} CH_3CH_2CH_2{-}\overset{\overset{\displaystyle CH_3}{|}}{\underset{\underset{\displaystyle CH_3}{|}}{C}}{-}OH$$

**4 a** Heat butan-1-ol under reflux with sodium bromide and concentrated sulfuric acid; distil to separate the product; shake in a separating funnel first with hydrochloric acid, then with aqueous sodium hydrogencarbonate to remove impurities; dry with anhydrous sodium sulfate; finally distil.

**b** Heat under reflux with excess acidified sodium dichromate(VI); distil off the product.

**c** Heat a mixture of 2-hydroxybenzoic acid and ethanoic anhydride under reflux with an acid catalyst; add water to hydrolyse the excess anhydride; pour into cold water and allow the product to crystallise; filter off the solid; recrystallise the solid using water as the solvent.

**5 a** 60% methanol
**b** 90% methanol

**6 a** Cyclohexene: decolourises a solution of bromine; does not react with $PCl_5$.

Cyclohexanol: does not react with a solution of bromine; produces acidic fumes of HCl(g) with $PCl_5$.

**b** 1-bromobutane and 1-iodobutane: warm with aqueous sodium hydroxide, acidify with dilute nitric acid and then add silver nitrate solution – cream precipitate from the bromo compound but a yellow precipitate from the iodo compound.

**c** Heat with acidic sodium dichromate(VI) which turns from orange to green with butan-2-ol but does not react with the tertiary alcohol, 2-methylpropan-2-ol.

**d** Butanal gives an orange-red precipitate on warming with Fehling's solution and a silver mirror with Tollens' reagent. Butan-1-ol does not react with either reagent.

**e** Butanoic acid gives an acidic solution in water while butan-1-ol is neutral in water. Butanoic acid gives carbon dioxide gas in a solution of sodium hydrogencarbonate while butan-1-ol does not react.

## Chapter 33

**1** X: $CH_3^+$
Y: $C_2H_5^+$
Z: $C_3H_7^+$

**2** 58

**3** $(CH_3)_3C^+$. This is a tertiary carbocation, which is more stable than secondary or primary carbocations because it is stabilised by the inductive effect of three alkyl groups, which helps to spread out the charge.

**4**

$$CH_3CH_2CH_2CH_2CH_2^+$$

Fragments to a positive ion and a free radical which is uncharged and not detected.

$$\nearrow \underset{15}{CH_3^+} + CH_3CH_2CH_2CH_2^\bullet$$
$$\underset{29}{CH_3CH_2^+} + CH_3CH_2CH_2^\bullet$$
$$\underset{43}{CH_3CH_2CH_2^+} + CH_3CH_2^\bullet$$
$$\underset{57}{CH_3CH_2CH_2CH_2^+} + CH_3^\bullet$$

**5** Q is $CH_3CH_2CHOHCH_3$. A secondary alcohol because it oxidises to a ketone R, not an aldehyde.

**6 a** Extensive conjugation (alternating double and single bonds) gives rise to coloured organic compounds. Conjugation is continuous throughout the molecule at pH 10. Conjugation is much less extensive at pH 1.

**b** The form at pH 10.

**7 a**

$$H{-}\overset{\overset{\displaystyle H}{|}}{\underset{\underset{\displaystyle H}{|}}{C}}{-}\overset{\overset{\displaystyle H}{|}}{\underset{\underset{\displaystyle H}{|}}{C}}{-}\overset{\overset{\displaystyle }{|}}{\underset{\underset{\displaystyle O}{||}}{C}}{-}\overset{\overset{\displaystyle H}{|}}{\underset{\underset{\displaystyle H}{|}}{C}}{-}H$$

**b** Peaks are in the ratio 2:3:3 and correspond to chemical shifts for R—CH$_2$—CO—R, R—CO—CH$_3$ and R—CH$_3$.

**c** Peak at 0.9 is coupled with 2 protons; so it will split into three peaks.
Peak at 2.1 is next to CO and uncoupled and will stay as a single peak.
Peak at 2.5 is coupled with 3 protons and will split into 4 peaks.

## AQA Chemistry

| Module | Chapters or sections to study in this guide | Notes |
|---|---|---|
| Module 1: Atomic structure, bonding and periodicity (AS) | 1, 2, 3, 6, 7 | Detail of 7.2 not required |
| Module 2: Foundation physical and inorganic chemistry (AS) | 4, 5, 8, 9, 10, 11 | This is a half unit, the rest is the practical assessment |
| Module 4: Further physical and organic chemistry (A2) | 18.1–18.4, 19, 20, 27.1–27.2, 28, 29, 30, 31, 32, 33 | Arrhenius equation not required in 18.4. Tri-iodomethane reaction not required in 28. Grignard reagents not included in 32 |
| Module 5: thermodynamics and | 21.1–21.3, 22, 23, 24.1–24.3, 25 | |

Module 6 includes assessment of practical skills and a synoptic paper to assess application of ideas from across the whole course.

## Edexcel Chemistry – specification A

| Module | Chapters or sections to study in this guide | Notes |
|---|---|---|
| Unit 1: Structure, bonding and main group chemistry (AS) | 1, 2, 3, 5, 6, 7, 8 | Analysis of bleach not required in 8.4 |
| Unit 2: Introductory organic chemistry, energetics, kinetics and equilibrium and applications (AS) | 4, 10, 11, 12, 13, 14, 15, 16, 17 | Details of organic reaction mechanisms not required here in 13, 14, 15 or 16 |
| Unit 4: Periodicity, quantitative equilibria and functional group chemistry (A2) | 19, 20, 22, 24, 26, 28, 29, 30.1, 30.3–30.4, 32.1 | Details of organic reaction mechanisms not required here in 28 |
| Unit 5: Transition metals, quantitative kinetics and applied organic chemistry (A2) | 5.2, 8.4, 13.2, 13.4, 14.3, 18, 21, 25, 27, 28.2, 30.2, 31, 32, 33 | |

Unit 3 assesses practical skills and knowledge in the AS course. Unit 6 includes assessment of practical skills and a synoptic paper to assess application of ideas from across the whole course.

## Edexcel Chemistry – specification B (Nuffield)

| Module | Chapters or sections to study in this guide | Notes |
| --- | --- | --- |
| Unit 1: Introductory chemistry (AS) | 1, 2, 3.2–3.4, 4.1–4.4, 5.1, 6, 7, 12.1–12.3, 15.1–15.2 | Only flame tests required in 7.2<br><br>Geometrical isomerism not required here in 12.3 |
| Unit 2: Bonding and reactions (AS) | 3.5–3.8, 4, 5, 8.1–8.3, 9.2, 10.1–10.2, 11.1–11.3, 12, 13, 14 | Markovnikov's rule not required in 13.3 |
| Unit 4: Energy and reactions (A2) | 18, 19, 20, 22, 23.1–23.2, 27, 28, 29 | |
| Unit 6: Applying chemistry (A2) | 21, 22, 24, 25, 26, 30, 31, 32, 33 | Grignard reagents not included in 32 |
| Units 3 and 5 cover the assessment of practical work and the Special Studies that are not covered by this Guide. | | |

## OCR Chemistry – specification A

| Module | Chapters or sections to study in this guide | Notes |
| --- | --- | --- |
| Module A: Foundation chemistry | 1, 2, 3, 5, 6, 7, 8 | Ideal gas equation not required in 3.1<br>No detail required from 7.2 |
| Module B: Chains and rings (AS) | 12, 13, 14, 15, 16, 17, 33.2 | |
| Module C1: How far, how fast? (AS) | 4, 10, 11 | This is a half module, C2/3 covers the assessment of practical skills |
| Module D: Chains, rings and spectroscopy (A2) | 26, 27, 28, 29, 30, 31, 33 | Tri-iodomethane reaction not required in 28 |
| Module E1: Trends and patterns | 7.4, 22.1, 24, 25 | A half module |
| Module F1: Unifying concepts | 18, 19, 20 | A synoptic half module. Arrhenius equation not required in 18.4 |
| The second test of module E assesses the optional topics that are not covered by this Guide. Module F2 covers assessment of practical skills. | | |

## OCR Chemistry – specification B (Salters)

This guide covers the chemical ideas in the Salters course but not the detail of the story lines.

| Module | Chapters or sections to study in this guide | Notes |
|---|---|---|
| Module 1: Chemistry for life (AS) | 1, 2.1–2.67, 3.1–3.5, 4, 6, 7.3, 12, 13.1, 16, 17, 23.1–23.2 | Ideal gas equation not required in 3.1 |
| Module 2: From minerals to medicines (AS) | 1.3, 2.8–2.9, 3.4, 3.6–3.7, 5, 7.1, 8, 9, 10, 11.1–11.3, 13.2–13.4, 14, 15, 27.3, 33.1–33.2 | Iodine-thiosulfate titrations not required in 8.4 <br><br> Principles not recall of detail in 9 <br><br> Markovnikov's rule not required in 13.3 |
| Module 4: Polymers, proteins (A2) | 3.6, 9.1, 18.1–18.3, 19.1, 21, 26, 29, 30.1, 30.4, 31, 33.4, 25 | |
| Module 5: Chemistry by design (A2) | 5, 19.2–19.3, 20, 22, 23.1–23.2, 24, 27.1–27.2, 28.1–28.2, 30.2, 32, 33 | Include the Haber process from 11.4 <br><br> Grignard reagents not included in 32 |

Modules 3 and 6 cover practical skills, investigations and other coursework

## WJEC Chemistry

| Module | Chapters or sections to study in this guide | Notes |
|---|---|---|
| Module CH1 (AS) | 1, 2.1–2.8, 3, 5, 6, 7, 7.1, 7.3, 8.1–8.2, 24 | Treatment of radioactive decay required but |
| Module CH2 (AS) | 2.9, 4, 10, 11, 12, 13, 16, 17, 19.1, 20.1–20.3 | Also included hydrolysis of halogenoalkanes from 14 and oxidation of alcohols from 15 |
| Module CH4 (A2) | 14, 15, 26, 27, 28, 29, 30, 31, 32, 33 | Iodine-thiosulfate titrations not required in 8.4 <br><br> Grignard reagents not included in 32 |
| Module CH5 (A2) | 5, 7, 8 18, 19, 20, 21, 22, 24, 25 | |

Module 3 assesses practical skills and the application of the ideas in modules CH1 and CH2 to practical activities. Module 6 includes practical assessment and a synoptic paper to assess application ideas from across the whole course.

## Northern Ireland Chemistry

| Module | Chapters or sections to study in this guide | Notes |
|---|---|---|
| Module 1: General chemistry | 1, 2, 3.2–3.5, 4, 5, 8, 12, 13, 16, 17.1, 21.3, 27.1–27.2 | Markovnikov's rule not required in 13.3 |
| Module 2: Physical, inorganic | 3.1–3.3, 3.6, 10, 11.1–11.3, 14, 15, 17.1, 18, 19, 20, 24, 25, 26, 28, 29 | Tri-iodomethane reaction not required in 28 |
| Module 3: Further physical, inorganic and organic chemistry | 3.1, 11.4, 22, 25.3, 25.4, 27.3, 30 | This Guide does not cover: details of sulfur chemistry, identification tests for ions, partition coefficients, Raoult's law or eutectic mixtures and alloys |

The fourth module is not covered in full by this guide. You have to study three out of five topics. Substantial parts, but not all, of the three of these topics are covered by this book; they are: Further inorganic chemistry, Electrochemistry and Analytical chemistry.

acids 48–9, 105–11
acid anhydrides 151–2, 155
acid-base equilibria 105–11
acid-base indicators 109–11, 156
acid-base reactions 48–9
acid-base titration 14–15, 109–11
acid chlorides 151–3, 155
acid dissociation constants, 108–11
acidic oxide 59–60, 91, 127
acid rain 91
acid strength 108–11
activation energy, 64–6, 98
acyl chloride 151–3, 155
addition-elimination reactions 152
addition polymerisation 81, 159
addition reaction 79–81, 146–8
alcohols 85–7, 165
aldehydes 86, 146–9, 165
alkalis 48–9
alkali metals 49–50
alkaline earth metals 50–1
alkanes 25, 73, 77–8, 88
alkenes 78–81, 165
aluminium 60–2
aluminium extraction 60–1
amides 151, 154
amines 144, 154–6
amino acids 156–7
ammonia 22, 49, 105–6, 132, 134, 154–5
ammonia manufacture 71, 103, 136
amount of substance 6, 8, 12–15, 17
amphoteric oxides 51, 127
anhydrides 151–2, 155
anions 19
anode 118
antiseptics 145
arenes 89, 141–5
aromatic hydrocarbons 89, 141
Arrhenius equation 98
atactic polymer 159
atomic number 1
atomic orbitals 3
atomic radius 45, 49–50
atomic structure 1–5
atomisation, enthalpy change of 120–1
autocatalysis 136
Avogadro constant 6
Avogadro's law 12
azo dyes 156

balanced equations 10, 41–2
base 49, 105–10, 156
basic oxide 50, 127
benzene 89, 141–4, 167
beryllium 51
bidentate ligands 132–3
biodegradable materials 161
blast furnace 59
bleach 56–7
boiling point 16–18, 21, 25–8, 44, 77, 141, 164
Boltzman distribution 65–6
bond dissociation enthalpy 36

bond enthalpies 32, 36–7, 77
Born-Haber cycle 120–2
bromine 39, 53–4, 103, 143
bromine extraction 57–8
Brønsted-Lowry theory 105–6, 127
buffer solutions 111

calcium carbonate 51
calorimeter 31–3
carbocations 80, 166
carbon 128
carbonates 50–2
carbonyl compounds 146–9
carboxylic acids 86, 150–3, 165
catalysts 63–6, 69, 89–91, 131, 136, 152
catalytic converter 91, 136
catalytic cracking 89
cathode 118
cations 19
cells 113–15
changes of state 66
chelates 133
chemical equations 9–10
chiral compounds 139, 157
chlor-alkali industry 57
chlorides 128–9
chlorine 2, 53–7, 127, 143
chlorine oxoanions 55–6
chlorine water treatment 56
chromium 131
cis-trans isomerism 75–6, 138
collision theory 64–6
colour of transition metal complex ions 135–6
colour in organic compounds 156
complex ions 131–5
concentrations 13–15, 94, 108
condensation polymers 159–60
conjugate acid-base pairs 106
conjugated system 167–8
Contact process 70–1
co-ordinate bond 22–3, 132–3
co-ordination compounds 22–3, 131–5
copper 132
corrosion 118
covalent bonds 21–4, 26–9, 36–7, 43, 127–8
covalent radius 45
cracking 77–8, 89–90, 92
cross linking 159
crude oil 88–90
crystal structures of ionic compounds 21, 123
crystal structures of metals 19
crystal structures of non-metals 26–8
curly arrows 78, 80

dative covalent bond 22–3, 105, 132–3, 143
d-block elements 43, 130–7
delocalised electrons 18–19, 141–5, 150, 156
diamond 27

diazonium salts 156
dipole-dipole interactions 24–5
dipoles 24–5
disinfectants 145
displacement reactions 53, 58
displayed formulae 74
disproportionation reaction 55–6, 116, 132
distillation 163
d-orbitals 130, 135–6
dot-and-cross diagrams 20, 22–3
double bonds 22, 79
dynamic equilibrium 68–9

edta 132–3
electrical conductivity 19, 21, 27–8
electrochemical cells 113–18
electrochemical series 115–17
electrode potential 114–17
electrolysis 20, 57, 60, 118
electrolysis of brine 57
electron affinity 120–1
electron configuration 3, 130
electron transfer 20, 39–40
electronegativity 24, 26, 28
electrophiles 80, 143–4
electrophilic addition 80
electrophilic substitution 142–5
electrostatic forces 122
elements 1
elimination reaction 83, 86–7
empirical formula 8–9, 73
enantiomers 139
endothermic changes 30, 37, 104
end point 14, 56
energy density of fuels 88
energy levels 3–4
enthalpy changes 30–7, 124–6
enthalpy change of atomisation 120–1
enthalpy change of combustion 31–5
enthalpy change of formation 33–6, 120–2
enthalpy change of hydration 122–3
enthalpy change of neutralisation 32–3
enthalpy change of reaction 35–7
enthalpy change of solution 123
entropy 124–5, 133
epoxyethane 90
equilibrium 68–72, 100–4, 113–19
esters 86, 151–2
ethanol 85–7, 90
ethene 79–81, 90
exothermic reactions 30, 37, 104, 124

fats 152
fatty acids 153
feasibility 125
Fehling's solution 86, 146–8
fermentation 87
fibres 158
first order reaction 95–6
flame tests 50, 52

fractional distillation 88, 163–4
fragmentation patterns 166
free energy changes 124–6
free radicals 78, 159
free-radical chain reactions 78, 159
Friedel-Crafts reaction 142, 144
fuels 87–9, 91–2
functional group 73, 138, 164–7
fundamental particles 1

gases 12, 16–17
gas-volume calculations 12–13
geometrical isomerism 75–6, 138
giant structures 18–19, 21, 43,
    127–8
graphite 27
Grignard reagents 162–3
group 43
group one 49–50
group two 39, 50–2
group four 26, 128–9
group seven 53–8

Haber process 71
half-equation 40, 113–16
half-life 95–6
halide ions 54–5
halogens 39, 53–8
halogenoalkanes 82–4, 144
Hess's law 34–6, 120–2
heterogeneous catalyst 136
heterogeneous equilibrium 103–4
heterogeneous reaction 63
heterolytic bond breaking (fission) 80
hexadentate ligand 132–3
Hofmann degradation 154
homogeneous catalyst 136
homogeneous equilibrium 70
homologous series 73
homolytic bond breaking (fission) 78
hydration 122–3
hydrocarbons 77–81, 88–91, 141–2
hydrogen bonding 25–6, 150, 167
hydrogen electrode 114–15
hydrogen halides 54
hydrogenation 136, 142
hydrolysis: 83, 99, 128, 134, 151–2,
    154
hydroxides 49–50

ice 26–7
ideal gases 17, 24
indicators 14, 56, 109–11
inductive effect 80–1
inert-pair effect 128
infra-red (IR) spectroscopy 86, 166–7
initial rate method 96–7
intermediate bonding 24, 122
intermolecular forces 24–6, 77
iodine 26, 39, 53–4
iodine-thiosulfate titrations 56–7
ionic bonding 19–21, 28, 121–2,
    127–8
ionic product of water 106
ionic radius 49–50, 52

ionisation enthalpy (energy) 4, 45–6,
    49–50
ionisation of water 106
iron 132
iron extraction 59
isomers 75, 138–9
isomerisation 89
isotactic polymer 158–9
isotopes 1–2

Ka 108–11
Kc 100–1, 103, 125
Kp 101–4
Kw 106
Kelvin tempraturee scale 17, 31
ketones 86, 146–9, 165
Kevlar 160
kinetic stability 66, 129
knocking 88

landfill 92–3
lattice 18, 120
lattice enthalpy (energy ) 120–3
Le Chatelier's principle 69–72,
    103–4, 111
lead-acid cell 117
leaving group 87
Lewis acid/bases theory 143–4
ligands 132–5
ligand substitution reactions 134
limiting reactant 11
liquids 16
lithium tetrahydridoaluminate(III) 147,
    150, 154
logarithms 106–9
lone pair of electrons 22–3, 105, 132

Markovnikov rule 79–80
mass number 1
mass spectrometry 2, 166
Maxwell–Boltzmann distribution
    65–6
mechanism of reactions 84, 99
melting point 16, 18, 21, 27–8, 44,
    164
metals 19–20, 43, 49–51
metal extraction 59–62
metallic bonds 18, 43, 127
molar mass 8, 17
molar volume 12–13
mole 6, 12
mole fraction 101–2
molecular formula 9, 73
molecule 21–9, 43, 127–8
monodentate ligands 132
monomers 81, 158–60
multiple bonds 22

names of carbon compounds 74–5
names of inorganic compounds 41
neutralisation reaction 49
nitrates 51
nitration of benzene 142–3, 155
nitric acid manufacture 71–2
nitriles 83, 154

noble gases 25, 127
non-metals 20, 43
non-polar solvent 78
NOx 91
nuclear magnetic resonance
    spectroscopy (nmr) 168–9
nucleophiles 84, 99, 147–8
nucleophilic addition 146–8
nucleophilic substitution 82–4, 99

optical isomers 138–9
orbitals 3
order of reaction 94–8
organic analysis 164–5
organic synthesis 162–5
oxidation 39–40, 60, 86, 113–18,
    142, 146
oxidation numbers 40–2, 55
oxidation states 55, 131, 134
oxides 49–50, 127, 129
oxidising agents 39–42, 53–4,
    115–17
oxoacids 41, 128
oxoanions 55
oxonium ions 105–9, 143

partial pressures 101
p-block elements 43
peptides 157
percentage composition 8
percentage yield 11
period 43
period three 127–9
periodic table 3, 43–6, 127–9, 190
periodicity of atomic properties 45–6
periodicity of chemical properties
    127–9
periodicity of physical properties
    43–4
peroxides 159
petrol 88–91
pH changes during titrations
    109–10
pH scale 106–11
phase 103
phenols 144–5
phenylamine 155–6
photochemical smog 91
physical properties 44
pi($\pi$)-bonds 79
pK 107, 109–11
plastics 92, 161
polar covalent bonds 24, 28
polar molecules 24, 123
polar solvents 122
polarisability 25, 28
polarised light 138–9
polarising power 28, 52, 134–5
pollution 91–3
polyamides 158–60
polyesters 158–60
polymers 81, 144, 158–60
polymerisation 81, 158–60
p-orbitals 3
pressure 12, 17

Study and Revise AS and A2 Level Chemistry

primary, secondary and tertiary organic compounds 82, 85–6
proteins 156–7
proton transfer 105–6

quaternary ammonium cations 155

racemic mixture 139
rate constants 94–7
rate determining step 99
rate equations 94–7
rates of reaction 63–7, 94–9
reacting masses 10
reacting volumes of gases 12–13
reaction kinetics 63–7, 94–9
reaction mechanisms 84, 99
real gases 17, 24
recycling 61–2, 92
redox equilibria 113–19, 132
redox reactions 39–42, 113–18
redox titration 56–7
reducing agents 39–42, 50, 54, 86, 115–17, 147
reduction 39–40, 50, 54, 86, 115–17, 147, 155
reference electrodes 115
refining of oil 88–9
reforming 89
relative atomic mass 2, 8
relative isotopic mass: 1
relative molecular mass 9, 73, 166
reversible reactions 68

salts 49
saturated compounds 77
s-block elements 43, 49–52
shapes of complex ions 133
shapes of molecules and ions 23–4
shells 3
shielding 4–5, 45
SI units 18
silver halides 56, 83, 132

skeletal formulae 74
SN1 and SN2 reactions 99
sodium chloride structure 21
sodium tetrahydridoborate(III) 147
sodium thiosulfate 56–7
solids 16
solubility 21, 27–8, 123
solvents 84, 87
s-orbitals 3
specific heat capacity 31
spectroscopy 86, 66–9
spin 3
spontaneous reaction 37, 117, 124
stability of benzene 142
stability of compounds 37, 52, 66, 121–2, 126, 133–4
standard electrode potentials 114–16, 125, 134
standard enthalpy changes 33–5, 126
standard free energy change 125–6
standard hydrogen electrode 114–15
standard molar entropy 124
standard solution 15
standard state 33
states of matter 16–17
state symbols 10
steel 59–61
stereoisomers 138
stoichiometry 10
strong acids 48, 106
structural formulae 74–6
structural isomers 75, 138
substitution reactions 77–8, 82–4, 142, 145
sulfates 51
sulfuric acid manufacture 70–1
surfactants 155
surroundings 30
synthesis of organic compounds 162–3

synthetic routes 162–3
system 30

temperature effect on equilibria 70–2, 103–4
temperature effects on reaction rates 63–5, 98
tests for functional groups 164–5
theoretical yield 11
thermal cracking 90
thermal decomposition 52
thermodynamic stability 37, 52, 66, 126
titanium 61
titanium extraction 61
titration 14–15, 56–7
Tollens' reagent 86, 146–8
transition metals 130–7
tri-iodomethane reaction 149

ultra-violet spectroscopy 167–8
unsaturated compounds 78

van der Waals forces 24
vanadium 131
vapours 17
vegetable oils 152
volume 12–15, 17

wastes 91–3
water treatment 56
wavenumber 167
weak acids 48, 108–11, 150
weak bases 108–9
word equations 9–10

yield calculations 11

zeolites 89
zwitterions 157

| | 1 | 2 | | | | | Group | | | | | | | 3 | 4 | 5 | 6 | 7 | 0 |
|---|---|---|---|---|---|---|---|---|---|---|---|---|---|---|---|---|---|---|---|
| **Period** | | | | | | | | | | | | | | | | | | | |
| 1 | 1<br>**H**<br>Hydrogen<br>1 | | | | | | | | | | | | | | | | | | 2<br>**He**<br>Helium<br>4 |
| 2 | 3<br>**Li**<br>Lithium<br>7 | 4<br>**Be**<br>Beryllium<br>9 | | | | | | | | | | | | 5<br>**B**<br>Boron<br>11 | 6<br>**C**<br>Carbon<br>12 | 7<br>**N**<br>Nitrogen<br>14 | 8<br>**O**<br>Oxygen<br>16 | 9<br>**F**<br>Fluorine<br>19 | 10<br>**Ne**<br>Neon<br>20 |
| 3 | 11<br>**Na**<br>Sodium<br>23 | 12<br>**Mg**<br>Magnesium<br>24 | | | | | | | | | | | | 13<br>**Al**<br>Aluminium<br>27 | 14<br>**Si**<br>Silicon<br>28 | 15<br>**P**<br>Phosphorus<br>31 | 16<br>**S**<br>Sulfur<br>32 | 17<br>**Cl**<br>Chlorine<br>35.5 | 18<br>**Ar**<br>Argon<br>40 |
| 4 | 19<br>**K**<br>Potassium<br>39 | 20<br>**Ca**<br>Calcium<br>40 | 21<br>**Sc**<br>Scandium<br>45 | 22<br>**Ti**<br>Titanium<br>48 | 23<br>**V**<br>Vanadium<br>51 | 24<br>**Cr**<br>Chromium<br>52 | 25<br>**Mn**<br>Magnesium<br>55 | 26<br>**Fe**<br>Iron<br>56 | 27<br>**Co**<br>Cobalt<br>59 | 28<br>**Ni**<br>Nickel<br>59 | 29<br>**Cu**<br>Copper<br>63.5 | 30<br>**Zn**<br>Zinc<br>65.4 | | 31<br>**Ga**<br>Gallium<br>70 | 32<br>**Ge**<br>Germanium<br>73 | 33<br>**As**<br>Arsenic<br>75 | 34<br>**Se**<br>Selenium<br>79 | 35<br>**Br**<br>Bromine<br>80 | 36<br>**Kr**<br>Krypton<br>84 |
| 5 | 37<br>**Rb**<br>Rubidium<br>85 | 38<br>**Sr**<br>Strontium<br>88 | 39<br>**Y**<br>Yttrium<br>89 | 40<br>**Zr**<br>Zirconium<br>91 | 41<br>**Nb**<br>Niobium<br>93 | 42<br>**Mo**<br>Molybdenum<br>96 | 43<br>**Tc**<br>Technetium | 44<br>**Ru**<br>Ruthenium<br>101 | 45<br>**Rh**<br>Rhodium<br>103 | 46<br>**Pd**<br>Palladium<br>106 | 47<br>**Ag**<br>Silver<br>108 | 48<br>**Cd**<br>Cadmium<br>112 | | 49<br>**In**<br>Indium<br>115 | 50<br>**Sn**<br>Tin<br>119 | 51<br>**Sb**<br>Antimony<br>122 | 52<br>**Te**<br>Tellurium<br>128 | 53<br>**I**<br>Iodine<br>127 | 54<br>**Xe**<br>Xenon<br>131 |
| 6 | 55<br>**Cs**<br>Caesium<br>133 | 56<br>**Ba**<br>Barium<br>137 | 57 ►<br>**La**<br>Lanthanum<br>139 | 72<br>**Hf**<br>Hafnium<br>178 | 73<br>**Ta**<br>Tantalum<br>181 | 74<br>**W**<br>Tungsten<br>184 | 75<br>**Re**<br>Rhenium<br>186 | 76<br>**Os**<br>Osmium<br>190 | 77<br>**Ir**<br>Iridium<br>192 | 78<br>**Pt**<br>Platinum<br>195 | 79<br>**Au**<br>Gold<br>197 | 80<br>**Hg**<br>Mercury<br>201 | | 81<br>**Tl**<br>Thallium<br>204 | 82<br>**Pb**<br>Lead<br>207 | 83<br>**Bi**<br>Bismuth | 84<br>**Po**<br>Polonium | 85<br>**At**<br>Astatine | 86<br>**Rn**<br>Radon |
| 7 | 87<br>**Fr**<br>Francium | 88<br>**Ra**<br>Radium<br>226 | 89 ►►<br>**Ac**<br>Actinium<br>227 | 104<br>**Rf**<br>Rutherfor-dium | 105<br>**Db**<br>Dubnium | 106<br>**Sg**<br>Seaborgium | 107<br>**Bh**<br>Bohrium | 108<br>**Hs**<br>Hassium | 109<br>**Mt**<br>Meitnerium | 110<br>**Uun**<br>Ununnilium | 111<br>**Uuu**<br>Unununium | 112<br>**Uub**<br>Ununbium | | | | | | | |

**Key:**

| |
|---|
| Atomic number<br>**Symbol**<br>Name<br>Relative atomic mass |

**Transition elements**

► **Lanthanoid elements**

| 58<br>**Ce**<br>Cerium<br>140 | 59<br>**Pr**<br>Praseo-dymium<br>141 | 60<br>**Nd**<br>Neo-dymium<br>144 | 61<br>**Pm**<br>Promethium | 62<br>**Sm**<br>Samarium<br>150 | 63<br>**Eu**<br>Europium<br>152 | 64<br>**Gd**<br>Gadolinium<br>157 | 65<br>**Tb**<br>Terbium<br>159 | 66<br>**Dy**<br>Dysprosium<br>163 | 67<br>**Ho**<br>Holmium<br>165 | 68<br>**Er**<br>Erbium<br>167 | 69<br>**Tm**<br>Thulium<br>169 | 70<br>**Yb**<br>Ytterbium<br>173 | 71<br>**Lu**<br>Lutetium<br>175 |
|---|---|---|---|---|---|---|---|---|---|---|---|---|---|

►► **Actinoid elements**

| 90<br>**Th**<br>Thorium<br>232 | 91<br>**Pa**<br>Protactinium<br>231 | 92<br>**U**<br>Uranium<br>238 | 93<br>**Np**<br>Neptunium<br>237 | 94<br>**Pu**<br>Plutonium | 95<br>**Am**<br>Americium | 96<br>**Cm**<br>Curium | 97<br>**Bk**<br>Berkelium | 98<br>**Cf**<br>Californium | 99<br>**Es**<br>Einstein-ium | 100<br>**Fm**<br>Fermium | 101<br>**Md**<br>Mendel-evium | 102<br>**No**<br>Nobelium | 103<br>**Lr**<br>Lawrecium |
|---|---|---|---|---|---|---|---|---|---|---|---|---|---|

**Note:** Relative atomic masses are shown only for elements which have stable isotopes or isotopes with a very long half-life.